The Advanced Patterns

Silvia Hartmann, PhD

First Edition 2003

Published by DragonRising

ISBN 1873 483 68 6

The Advanced Patterns Of EFT
©Silvia Hartmann 2002

ISBN 1873 483 68 6
Published by
DragonRising
18 Marlow Avenue
Eastbourne BN22 8SJ
United Kingdom
http://dragonrising.com

Other Titles By This Author:

Adventures In EFT
Project Sanctuary
Energy Healing For Animals
The Story Teller
Oceans Of Energy - Patterns & Techniques of EmoTrance™ Vol. 1
In Serein

Printed & bound by Antony Rowe Ltd, Eastbourne

Acknowledgements

With Gratitude To:

Gary Craig, Creator of Emotional Freedom Techniques EFT for giving the World this most amazing tool for growth, learning and healing;

My friends and colleagues from The AMT, and especially Chrissie Hardisty, Susan Courtney, Ananga Sivyer and Nicola Quinn;

The members of Meridiantherapy Newsgroup;

My readers, clients and students for helping me develop these patterns and teaching me about everything I have ever learned;

And to Alex Kent whose unfailing support has meant the world to me.

Table Of Contents

Introduction by Silvia Hartmann, PhD

Welcome to the Advanced Patterns of EFT.

The Story So Far ...

Here we are, coming up for the turning of the year into 2003.

I have been working with Energy Psychology or Meridian Therapies, and most specifically, with EFT, for five years now.

My background is passionately in personal development and not in psychology. This is an important distinction and will become clear later on; for now, it would suffice to say that my focus is always and virtually exclusively on the client's side.

I see everything from the client's point of view.

I know myself quite well, and one thing I know most profoundly is my own resistance to change and to do the things I consciously know are good for me. I also know that no matter how smart I am, when the chips are down, it is my emotions who will win out in a straight conflict, time and time again, and they will drive my behaviour - not common sense, and often not even prior experience, no matter how traumatic it might have been.

I am also extremely obsessive once I get going.

In 1987, I purchased my very first Personal Development product ever. At that time, I was a companion animal behaviour specialist and had never really had an interest in the ways of the human mind. For some reason, an advertisement from the famous Nightingale Conant company caught my eye and I bought myself as a birthday present a 6 tape set by Brian Tracy called The Psychology of Achievement.

I remember the moment well.

I closed the office door behind me, put the tape on, lay down on the carpet with my arms behind my back and began to listen to Mr Tracy's wonderfully modulated and very American voice, and I fell in love in an instant.

This was the first time in my entire experience on this planet so far that someone seemed to think like I did, that someone admitted to the problems that I have always had but that are not talked about amongst "normal" people - something that can be forgotten too easily when one's entire set of friends derive from the therapist's community.

It was also really the first time that I got the idea that you actually can make changes in your life, that you don't have to put up with your personal miseries, whatever they may be, and that there could be a hope of something better, for you.

From that moment forth, my obsession kicked in and I began to study the field of personal change with a vengeance. If you don't know me, what that means is that I stop whatever else takes my time, and from the second I get up in the morning to the very last thought I have at night, I don't do anything else but to learn, to wonder and to question about some aspect relating to my area of interest.

Yes, it was tough on the family! And yes, it still is!

But it has its good points.

If you apply yourself like this to any given topic, you can really learn pretty fast about a great many things.

I went through quite a bit of the available literature on the various fields of psychology and personal development. I must admit that although some of it was very interesting, it didn't seem to be too practical and it was all such a lot of hard work, it made me sigh just reading it.

I studied hypnosis in some depth and found it fascinating indeed; fascinating enough at any rate to take a number of different trainings by a number of different trainers from various different angles on the field. From there, I went to NLP and that was a revelation. I'll take a moment to tell you that NLP is the most useful thing that I have ever learned, ever - and if I had to live on a desert island and could choose just the one thing to take with me, I would take NLP and not the energy therapies, so that is saying something!

Then I came across EFT and of course, immediately ordered Gary Craig's tape set, then whatever else there was out there on the subject and started to experiment with it in earnest.

I was and am still profoundly impressed with the results I was getting for myself and for my clients at the time. Now here was something that really worked and you did not have to be Einstein to make it work, a most important point indeed because if you're really switched on and congruent, everything works, more or less. However, I'm rarely both at the same time and neither are my clients, so to have these approaches for us imperfect individuals was a tremendous gift indeed.

This book is primarily written for people who work with EFT or at least compatible meridian/energy therapies. If you have little or no experience with these therapies, please go now and get your education in their theories and professional usage; it won't take long, isn't very expensive and will prove to be the best gift you will have ever given to yourself, your friends and loved ones, and your clients.

Many of the patterns in this book simply cannot be approached without these therapies to any degree of safety and you should not attempt to recreate some of these patterns, and especially not the Guiding Star set or the Redemption Set but also Crime Line, Shadow Emotions and Loss of Life if you have no knowledge of the application of EFT.

The reason for the above Safety Note is that only the meridian/energy therapies can do something reliably which is an absolute turning point in my opinion for the entire human race - namely, put us in a position where we no longer have to be afraid of our emotions.

The fear of fear, pain, love, loneliness, desolation, terror and agony runs a very great many, if not all, of our strange human strategies that cause so much inter- and intra-personal conflict. The new meridian/energy therapies and most of all, their Ambassador EFT release us from this bondage and set us free in a way that is so profound, so "above and beyond", that even many practitioners in the field haven't quite got their heads around it yet.

Before we begin, I would like to explicitly state that this is not a self help manual although of course you will find many techniques and approaches that you can use for yourself as well as with your clients.

"Advanced Patterns of EFT" is a manual for practitioners, i.e. people who are using EFT with a variety of presenting problems and a variety of presenting people in a professional setting.

When I wrote "Adventures" (and if you have not read "Adventures In EFT" yet, I would strongly recommend that you do, for the underlying principles of the craft are in that book and are not repeated here, as well as all the learnings from Adventures being absolutely pre-supposed) I focussed on making sure that the basics of EFT were kept intact and complete in all ways.

I did this because it was then and still is now my belief that a full grounding in the Classic EFT routine as it stands and applying it exactly as it comes is one of the best teaching systems to learn about the connections between neurology, physiology, and the connector plane energy systems and beyond which has been invented to date.

I still hold that a decent apprenticeship served with EFT is probably the best step stone you can give yourself for you future explorations and discoveries of your own.

I presume that you have served this apprenticeship and are now in your Journeyman stage, ready for more advanced work and more complex applications and variations on the treatment's presuppositions, treatment procedures and routines.

This book is a collection of such patterns and techniques.

None of these patterns are designed in any way to replace the Classic EFT technique. These are fine tuning mechanisms, special tools for special circumstances and best considered to be add-ons to the mainstay of the Classic EFT protocol usage such as The Story Protocol, The Keyword Protocol and other basic techniques which can be found in detail in "Adventures In EFT".

The fascinating aspect about the patterns and techniques in this collection is that they have something in common – namely that in the very application of EFT in these ways, we learn something very important not just about how our neurologies and energy bodies work, but also **what else can be done** to improve the way we think, we treat ourselves and how we do therapy with others.

EFT is a fantastic tool. It is so incredibly flexible, it can be applied in the most astonishing ways to clear trauma, soothe stressed out energy systems and to "open the doors of perception" when the confusion recedes and clarity is restored.

I personally hold the Classic EFT Protocol in the highest esteem possible and these articles, protocols and therapeutic patterns are designed to use the fantastic tool that is Emotional Freedom Techniques on a whole new level of elegance and mastery.

I trust you will find something in these pages that will be useful to you and your clients and I offer these patterns and my sincere best wishes to you,

Silvia Hartmann

Nov 27th, 2002

PART 1 - ELEGANCE IN THE EFT PROCESS

The EFT Treatment Flow

Before we go into the advanced patterns, I would like to begin with the general EFT treatment flow which occurs in every session and even holds for self treatments.

Every aspect of this progression contributes to the overall success of using EFT to its best abilities and therefore, each one must be given due care and consideration.

EFT Session Progression

1. Introduction Phase

- Create Rapport (aligning the energy systems of therapist and client so the therapist may know what is going on with the client; in self help, this would be getting into rapport with oneself as one sits down quietly and begins to consider the problem).

- Take Details (in therapy/counselling etc. this would be the intake forms and technical details; in self help this would be to consider the details and circumstances of the problem).

- Enquire Problem/s (find out what the problem is about, what its components are and what other factors might be relevant).

- Contract/Agreement (what are we working on, how do we know when we have achieved what outcome, how do we test it and how do we know we are done – the goal of the treatment, if you will).

2. Contacting The Problem

- Formulating Opening Statements (this is simply the act of talking about the problem in order to discover the most direct and effective Opening Statements or set ups for the treatment phase).

3. The Treatment Phase

- Conducting EFT Treatments (now, we tap on the Opening Statements we have decided upon in phase two and the session unfolds as we clear opening statements and the client responds).

- Aspects (in the treatment phase, we discover aspects of the problem, unexpected linkages to other problem groups, make discoveries about the nature of the problem and so forth).

- First Tests (bearing in mind the original goal of the treatment, which may or may not have changed during the treatment so far if more important problems or aspects were uncovered, we will at some point begin the first testing procedures to check if the problem has been significantly reduced or entirely resolved. These first tests will lead either to more treatments as more aspects are uncovered, or to the closure phase of the treatment.)

4. Closure Phase

- Testing (this would be the final test on the problem. Although in EFT treatments it is often presumed that "one session will cure all", this final test might reveal that more work needs to be done or that we are dealing with a large interlinked problem group that needs more time and treatments to be fully resolved. Also, some problems are such that only "time will tell" as to whether they really have been entirely resolved and the client has to go back to their normal environments and situations to know if the treatment has really worked).

- Contract/Agreement Revisited (All kinds of things can happen in an EFT session which are absolutely unpredictable. Here, we need to sum up what has happened and how, why or if we have diverged from our original goal for the treatment session. This is essential to retain an overview of what is going on, and just as important for self treatments as it is for client/therapist situations to remain clear on where we are and what we need to do next.

- Homework Assignments/Support (Here, we make sure that everyone knows what, if anything, needs to be done after the treatment session to foster and maintain the changes, to stabilise the gains and to make sure that what was healed during the session stays healed. In therapy, one would discuss the feedback arrangements, such as telephone check-backs, another session, what the client is to do when they are at home, and so forth. For self help, it is also useful to make sure one is clear in one's own mind as to what should happen next).

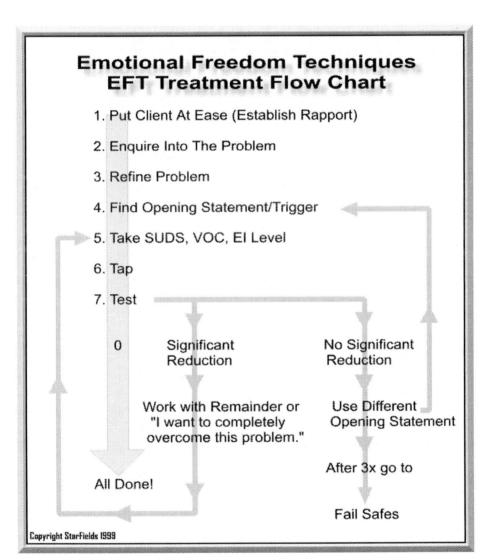

Building Rapport With Clients & The Public

We, who have been working with these techniques for many years now, can easily forget that to most people even the concept of people having meridians in their bodies which are invisible is really quite out of this world still.

For EFT treatments with the general public, it helps to remember this at all times; and this chapter represents an overview of the issues involved in building rapport with clients, participants and the general public so as many people as possible may be able to come forward and reap the rewards from entering into these energetic processes for healing, de-stressing and bringing about real and lasting positive changes in their lives.

Public Presentation Of EFT

This would be the first contact the potential clients or seekers have with not only the technique but also with you as the representative of the entire field of energy/meridian therapies as a whole.

This first contact occurs through publicity efforts on your behalf of some kind - this may be advertising, telling people about it, public demonstrations at health fayres and shows, personal demonstrations to key people at health centres, sports centres, holistic centres, radio shows, TV, and even what you put on your web site or into practitioner listings.

We are holding here a most profoundly two edged sword.

One the one edge is the fact that EFT is profoundly effective when it is done well and really can make inroads into most every presenting problem anyone could bring to your door - from Aardvark phobia to Zuluitis. This is true and we know this BUT.

The other edge of our profound sword is that stating all of that will probably cause the opposite of what we have in mind for most people; rather than causing them to think, wow, this is great, they'll probably think, yeah right, that and Dr Snake's Health Oil.

Personally, I have found it useful to go the other way in my explanations of EFT and all I say these days is that it does only one single thing - it releases negative emotions.

"Would that be useful to you?"

No matter what the circumstance, be it cancer or golf, dyslexia or hay fever, DID or MPS, childbirth or bereavement, addiction to phobia, the answer to that question is always a resounding "Yes!".

We know that emotional drivers are at the root of most, if not all, diseases of the mind and body and that by releasing the core emotional drivers and returning the whole system to a state of calm and balance, all these many longstanding physiological and psychological problems can simply melt way but it has been my experience that you can't tell people that straight to their face and not expect a huge backlash of disbelief, distrust, fear of disappointment (again!) and all kinds of other negativity that isn't necessary if you focus and target your explanations to your specific audience at the time and leave out all that is not relevant to them at this point.

There are two reasons why selling EFT like snake oil is counter productive and will cause more trouble than its worth:

1. The majority of people who should learn it will reject such approaches immediately - nurses, care workers, support staff, reporters, allopathic practitioners and indeed, any Westerner who has any kind of self concept as being sensible, rational and "no fool". Once they are in the rejection mode, you have to move mountains to change their minds again - if they had been approached just a little more softly, this initial rejection need never happen.

2. The rest might have completely unrealistic expectations of what the technique can do. Oh, it can do a great deal, but it can't change a great many things - the life you've led, the size of your feet and so many other things that simply are. Also, it is not practical nor even legal to promise instant cancer remission or making the blind see in a single session.

Great as the techniques are, we are dealing with highly complicated systems with two arms and on legs and we simply cannot ever be 100% sure that indeed, all the problems will be overcome quickly and right away.

To overcome this problem, I suggest two courses of action.

The first is to limit oneself to a particular field and concentrate on the uses, effects and benefits of the technique in that particular field.

For example, if one was to particularly address autism in children, to collect appropriate case histories, have a good old think about a theoretical proposition that might at least seem to explain WHY it works and HOW it works, to be familiar with the particular emotional and practical challenges in that one field and to speak the language correctly will produce an introduction to those who are actually in that field - practitioners as well as those who live with and around the problem - that will raise interest and have the people there come forward to find out more.

This is the absolute key to having people come into meridian and energy therapies and the role of EFT - to be an ambassador to a whole new realm of empowerment and healing.

Ambassadors are diplomats.

They respect the customs of the countries they find themselves in and learn their language before they say anything at all. If they did not, diplomatic relationships break off and we find ourselves at war, needlessly and to the detriment of all concerned.

We, likewise, must create through our advertising and presentation an atmosphere of interest and excitement, whilst not contravening the laws of those to whom we speak and with whom we are trying to communicate.

I said there were two ways to have people come forward with interest and wanting to find out more. The first one was to be very specific when speaking to a specific audience.

To speak to a global audience, one by needs must be global and focus on the very global effects of EFT - relaxation, calmness, releasing stress, releasing fear.

That is believable, possible and sounds certainly like something that would be useful and desirable.

Further, as the ones who have come forward and tried it are amazed and delighted that they got more than we promised to start with, there is no disappointment, no angry backlash and this will help to spread the word and have even more people come forward and just try it out for themselves - which is always the outcome of our advertising efforts, to get to a place where people will give EFT a chance.

Attunement In EFT Treatments

If you recall, Gary Craig's EFT "discovery statement" says that, "All negative emotions are caused by an imbalance in the energy system."

It is worth bearing in mind that EFT is a very abbreviated protocol form that is based on another, or rather if you will, **the** original meridian/energy therapy, namely Thought Field Therapy, researched and created by Dr Roger Callahan.

All of this has been taken out of the public explanations of EFT in order to make it more accessible and less "spooky" to the man and woman in the street, yet of course it remains by pre-supposition and in the act of **attuning to the problem** which is the central, original and fundamental difference between all meridian therapies and all of energy psychology as opposed to classic massage, acupuncture, acupressure or even the more advanced energy treatments such as Reiki.

It is only in meridian/energy therapies that the client is asked to "focus on the problem" with their intention **whilst the treatment is being delivered** – by thinking about it, being in touch with it, being in the presence of it and of course, by speaking about it (the opening or set up statement and reminder phrase).

So we have another, separate step there which is not talked about in basic EFT and the discovery statement thereby could read:

All negative emotions are caused by an imbalance in the energy system, and that in turn is caused by attuning to thoughtfields that negatively affect the balance of the energy system.

In my experience, the effectiveness of any of the meridian/energy therapies is directly proportional to the ability of the practitioner to create an environment whereby the client will feel safe to contact their negative emotions.

EFT does not work when it is not targeted correctly - no emotions to clear, no clearing, to put it in a nutshell.

A lack of rapport from the practitioner with a client who is not given to allowing themselves easy access to emotionally charged memories or states will preclude the techniques from working.

There is even a portion of the population - overwhelmingly men - who are so deeply disassociated from their own emotional processes that they can't access emotions at all. I have worked with a large number of these simply because I am at the end of a chain of referrals and it represents some fascinating challenges that require high levels of skill and the ability to really respond to the idiosyncratic manifestations of an individual client to make the treatment work. I would estimate the occurrence of this at about 5-8% of the population.

So what we have here is the following three requirements to make EFT work to its maximum potential:

- The client needs to be able to attune to the disturbance via the emotions which are the markers to the existence of the disturbance as well as being the drivers behind their problem behaviours/manifestations.

- In order to do this, the client must feel safe with the practitioner in the first place.

- When they do, it is in the practitioner's ability to receive from the client the information where exactly the disturbance is located as to how fast and successful the intervention will succeed.

The three points above are absolutely crucial and absolutely central to your abilities to help people make profound changes and to use these techniques with the power they were designed to be used.

Feeling Safe With The Practitioner

Sometimes, the term "rapport" in order to describe the practitioner and client being in a place of trust and understanding.

However, this is very misleading. Rapport means that two or more people are in the **same** place – whatever kind of state this might be.

If you have a client who is very disturbed, afraid, crying, shaking, **the last thing you want to do** is to go there and be there, too – an utterly resourceless state that does neither of you any good whatsoever.

Rapport is nothing but a device or a first step in a sequence of events which will have the client be in a reasonably balanced state before any intervention proceeds at all and to keep them there, with you being the safety anchor, the guide with the lantern, the guy rope, or whatever you wish to term the job of the practitioner who helps and guides the client through concluding their experiences.

The rapport state, i.e. the state within yourself that resonates with the client's internal state at the time and that gives you vital information on that client's processes, as well as giving the client a sense of familiarity and trust that you understand and that you are entirely respectful of their experiences, learnings, states and being, could be viewed as an attunement to the client's predominant thoughtfields at that time.

Attuning To Another

This means really nothing more than to turn your attention to another person and their energetic states of being, and then making a conscious effort to get into sync with them. This can be achieved by speeding yourself up or slowing yourself down until you notice a synchronisation taking place – there is a kinaesthetic feedback you will receive when you **click into rapport** with the other. As soon as you have achieved this, you will be able to have a sense of what it is like to be this person, and information about the person and their set-ups flows to you at an extremely rapid rate. Most of this information is below the threshold of conscious awareness and takes the form of an intuitive knowing just what to say, what to do and where to tap when this process is working as it should.

Some things that might help you to begin with are:

- Movements, breathing, voice and speech. These are all outward manifestations of inner states and quite cohesive energetically – someone who is stressed and thinking fast, with their thoughts tumbling this way and that, shows this blatantly on the outside with short, shallow breaths, fast words that stumble across each other, fast hand gestures that are not smooth, and a whole lot of tension in various parts of their bodies.

- Someone who is energetically slow and "depressed" will speak more slowly, slump in their seat or their shoulders when standing, their voice will be lower and their breathing slower.

- You can guide yourself into the right direction energetically by practically copying some of these outward manifestations or speeding and slowing your own thoughts in response.

It is always worthwhile, no matter how experienced one may perceive oneself to be, to practise these movements of energetic attunement with an open mind and on a regular basis because it makes you both far more aware of energetic mind body states as well as training your own flexibility in accessing different types of states fast and reliably.

Centring The Client

Once a level of attunement has been achieved, movements in **your** energy states bring about corresponding movements in the energy states of the second person because your systems have become interlinked.

It is good practise to "stabilise" a client before any investigation into what one might treat even begins, i.e. to have them be reasonably calm and relaxed and as neutral as possible, comfortable with where you are, comfortable with you, and ready in body and in mind to begin the exploration into the nature of their problem/s.

This **stable state is your baseline comparison** for all the changes from there you may be observing as the treatment and the preparation for the treatment unfold; it is also the state you need to **return your client to at the end of the session**. This basic stable state is your guideline and measure to know exactly what is happening **inside** the client without having to guess and often, without having to ask.

Please note that in general, people's "stable baseline state" is **not** a nicely relaxed, balanced affair at all.

Everyone has underlying tensions and disturbances, and beneath, a structure of habitual levels of disturbances of all kinds. A person might be twitching as a matter of course and that would be their baseline "stable" state; in moments of high disturbance, they twitch more or harder.

Be sure to note the idiosyncratic, habitual disturbances that are expressed in the baseline state such as:

- Muscle Tensions (unusual body alignment, neck position, spinal alignment etc)

- Rigidity in parts of the body or overall posture

- Level of activity (in movements, gestures, blinking, breathing)

- Facial Expressions (how quickly they change, which ones appear repeatedly)

- Skin appearance (colour, tone, temperature, moisture)

- Movements (neck, head, eye movements, hands, feet, shoulders in particular)

Once there is an understanding of the qualities and manifestations of the baseline state, it becomes easy to note and track any diversions from there and to use those as a guide in the formulation of attuning statements as well as to check back on the changes which have happened as a result of the treatments.

Client Preferences & Suitability For EFT Treatments

EFT Is NOT For Everyone Or For Everything

Read the above headline again – EFT is not for everyone, and it is not for everything.

EFT will not work if:

- the client practically cannot contact emotions or thoughfields, has no idea where a disturbance could be located, doesn't display disturbances in his physicality because the connection between the conscious mind and the energy body has become functionally detached;

- the client rejects EFT and actively refuses to tune into a problem and/or when forced to tap against their will, tenses up against the treatment and just shouts, "No!" inside themselves whilst they grit their teeth;

- the client gets angry and/or disturbed at the whole concept and/or the treatment routine (this can happen with very religious people who highly treasure their world view constructs and including some scientists).

Any practitioner worth their salt should watch out for such occurrences and responses and immediately do something about it – change the way they explain EFT, or simply drop it and do something else instead.

Further, EFT is not suitable for **all problems**.

This is not a conflict with the EFT adage of "Try it on everything!"

Of course you can **try it on everything** – indeed I also recommend you do. But then, take a note of what happens next and proceed in the light of your discoveries.

If the client says, for example, no I just want to talk, I don't like this, then that is what should happen. If you are getting a sense that you are heading for a major abreaction and you feel that isn't the way to go with a particular client, stop it and do something else instead. If nothing whatsoever happens after a good application set, once again, stop it and do something else instead rather than trying to convince yourself and/or the client that something really did happen only we didn't notice any results or effects.

This is straightforward enough but I wanted to make it clear and say it publicly as this entire book is full of EFT patterns. They don't all work with every client, they are not all suitable for every client, and one must **always** work with the feedback from the client to find the most suitable approach that will lead to the client being positive, proactive and excited about the goals and processes of their healing journey.

Flowing With The Client Preferences

It is **essential** in professional practise to have respect for a client's preferences in how to proceed with treatments.

For this we must firstly be very, **very** clear on one thing, namely that **your** preferences are not **my** preferences and for you to presume that they are would make me very unhappy - **and vice versa**.

Some people – and myself included – really are in the field of personal development, psychology and so forth because they are absolutely fascinated by the workings of their mind and at the end of the day, don't particularly want to be any happier or healthier but have the **WHY** question answered.

For such people, offering a quick fix solution is entirely beside the point and will meet with intensive resistance – the WHY people just want to know more, have insights, understandings and to this end, want to explore aspects, root causes and how it all hangs together.

You would find these people want to talk about their issues, about their thoughts on the issues and they seek feedback and further illumination in preference to – yes, **in preference to**! – problem solution and symptom cessation if they were forced to make the choice with a gun held to their heads.

There are other people who don't care what, why or even how but sincerely just want the problem solved and the symptoms to cease.

These people, when met with a therapist who is very keen on exploring root causes, get frustrated, fed up and resistant just as the people who want to explore get very frustrated if someone won't let them explore but just seeks to fix their problems as quickly and as economically as possible.

Now there are no merit badges for being in one or the other group, and neither is better or worse – it is a personal preference and "it simply is, as it is".

It is truly central to know firstly who you are, and secondly what kind the client is before you, and to find some middle ground for the treatment to be as effective as it could be.

It also serves to save you personally from inordinate frustration over "client resistance" and get you much better feedback from your past clients.

The Concept Of Client Avidity

In the treatment flow, once we have established a stable baseline state, we can begin our work of healing and restoration together with the client.

Clearly, EFT treatments are not something that the practitioner or therapists perpetrates on an anaesthetized, lifeless client who passively allows to happen whatever the therapist decides to do.

EFT treatments are a co-operative venture between client and therapist in every sense of the word and so it is important that both should be positive, excited and proactive about what is to come next, namely the treatments which will resolve the problem the client has brought to the session.

It was with a degree of shock and horror that I learned at some point that in psychology, there are only two ways in which a client is thought to respond to the therapists efforts to help them overcome a problem, namely:

Client Resistance – when a client fights the therapist and

Client Compliance – where they do as the therapist suggests.

Now frankly, I really think that sucks and that's a technical term!

What we are looking for is something altogether different when we are working with clients, namely a forward pointing state in which the client aligns with us and both of us really put our minds, hearts and souls forward to resolve the problem, with volition and desire.

I call this third option:

- **Client Avidity**

This is the state we need to evoke in the client if we want to have them succeed in whatever it is they are hoping to achieve from their EFT treatments because only in this third, forward pointing state are they truly committed to doing what needs to be done in all ways.

Pre-Problem Solving

Many of the higher end types of problems cannot be resolved successfully or even begin to unravel unless certain issues are addressed before we even start.

Most especially with addictions of all kinds (from cocaine to work, and from emotional state addictions to chocolate cookies) but also with chronic pains and any other form of chronic problem (from depression to money troubles and recurring relationship issues and so forth), there are issues that if they are not addressed, the problem will not "open itself up to treatment" for you and the client.

If you find that the treatments are not working or the client is "resisting" in any shape or form, you might need to deal with some of the following considerations up front:

- Issues of identity: I would cease to be ME without the problem; I would have to become someone else without the problem, the problem **is a part of me** (see also relationship with the problem).

- Issues of deservability, permission, possibility – I don't deserve to overcome this problem; it is impossible to overcome this problem, I'm not allowed to overcome this problem and so forth.

- Relationship with the problem: I need this problem, I love my problem, I rely on my problem, I am terrified to lose my problem.

- Fears of change and no change: I can't imagine life without the problem, there will be more problems if I release this problem, if we try and fail this time, it will be worse than not even having tried at all, etc.

- Fears of the process: I am scared of what I might find out about myself if we work on the problem, I don't want to know anything about the problem, I don't want to face the problem, I am afraid of the emotional pain the treatment might cause me.

As usual, we could make lists that are longer than the Human Genome Project but in the end, just asking the client up front what their fears and reservations might be, and asking them also how they would like to proceed, and where they would like to start, is the very best, most ecological and most profoundly appreciated way of responding to any form of conscious or unconscious "client resistance".

In keeping with the aim and goal of always having "client avidity" all through the treatments, it is very valuable to explain to clients that any form of resistance, such not liking something, struggling against it, having to use willpower to "make themselves do something" (and including complying with the therapists suggestions and instructions!) is always a sign of something in need of treatment and really nothing else.

If the client understands this frame of reference, they can really get involved very personally and from their end, help the therapist immeasurably by saying, for example, "Oh, I'm having a strong feeling that this is not a good idea.", which is a thousand times more helpful to the entire process of problem resolution than tight lipped silence or pretending to go along just fine, then leaving the office and declaring the treatment or the therapist to have been a total waste of time.

EFT & Order and Sequence

This chapter deals with not the order and sequence of tapping point, but the order and sequence of all the aspects which, together, make up the presenting problem group.

Certain problems cannot be resolved until they are resolved in the right order and sequence.

A ship cannot leave a harbour successfully until the crew is on board, the anchor has been lifted, the ropes tying it to the quay released and the engines switched on - and all of this needs to happen in the right order and sequence or else the whole process simply gets nowhere at all.

Here is an example of how this works in problem solving with EFT treatments.

Jerry had a problem with public speaking. He would freeze up entirely and described the sensation in these words, "It was as though there was a giant block between me and the people I am supposed to be talking to, like they are on the other side of a thick, high wall and I can't reach them at all, can't talk to them at all."

He was telling me this because he had tried every form of opening statement to get this "giant block" or "high wall" out of the way and it simply wouldn't budge - the EFT treatment wasn't working at all, there was no movement, no matter how hard and how long he would tap. I had an immediate sense of danger come to me and asked him, "Imagine for a moment if that wall wasn't there, what would it be like trying to speak to a group of people?"

He went as white as a sheet, started to tremble visibly and nearly stuttered as he said, "No, no I couldn't stand the criticism!" "Ok, put it back as it was, quickly."

He relaxed immediately but was still shaken from the experience which had shown us clearly that the wall was not the problem, but a solution to a problem that clearly needed to be solved first before the wall could come down.

In general, when confronted with a problem that won't budge, it is always useful to ask firstly, "What would happen if this problem wasn't there any longer?"

This brings up, as it did with Jerry, most likely two further or deeper problems to which the original problem may well have been the solution so far, namely:

1. **What you HAVE** or what has happened to make it impossible to NOT have the problem This includes bad memories, traumatic events and decisions, negative emotions such as fear, terror; expectations of failure and of bad outcomes, bad things you were told and you remember always, beliefs about genetic or character defects, etc.

2. **What you DON'T have** but you need in order to be able to deal with these situations. This usually includes all kinds of attributes such as strength and courage, talent, creativity, intelligence, good looks, the right ethnic origin, the right gender, the right connections, luck, God's support or even a shining track record of previous successful attempts.

In Jerry's case, what he did have was a number of very traumatic school experiences that had taught him it simply wasn't safe to make contact with people in public situations, and life long beliefs about himself resulting from this.

We began tapping on these and once in a while, I would ask him about the wall and it was getting a little smaller but showed no sign of disappearing altogether. So we went to what he didn't have but needed profoundly to make it be safe for him to face a group of people and feel safe and confident in doing so.

He said that he didn't have the strength and courage necessary to face the criticism and not to fall apart. We tapped on these separately: "Even though I don't have the strength to face angry people." which led straight into watching his father beat his mother and being too afraid to come to her aid.

And then, "I don't have the courage to stand up to bullies."

This was a very emotional round of tapping and when that was done, the wall had gone. All that was now left was insecurity and a feeling that he just didn't have any experience with public speaking - it had all stopped when the wall had been built all those years ago.

Jerry went on to take part in a public speaking course to get some experience now in a safe environment to make up for this lost "practise time" and the wall never came back.

The two questions of "What do I have that makes this happen?" and "What don't I have but is needed to end this problem/situation?" are very useful when a problem seems to be stuck.

If you consider the Order and Sequence of the overall problem and its own ecology, there are sometimes other questions to help discover what needs to be done first before this can happen, such as: "What do we need to do BEFORE you can release this problem?" This question gets some very interesting answers from different people.

One lady said, "I would have to promise to take care of myself much better if I was ever allowed to be in that situation again." This led to a sub-set problem group with its own aspects, and as in the example with Jerry, once THIS was "out of the way", the previously unmovable problem could be tapped away with total ease.

I find it fascinating how our mind-body systems can **switch off** the effectiveness of the EFT treatment if it's deemed that by taking something away - a problem or more likely, a protective device - the person will be worse off than they were before. It can, however, **switch them back on** just as astonishingly quickly again when these very real reservations have been laid to rest.

Rhythm, Pulse & Percussion In Tapping Treatments

It is interesting to observe people "tapping themselves".

People have very different natural rhythms, and then there's of course a great variance in how hard or softly someone taps.

Some tap very half heartedly, barely touching the spots at all, others tap so hard it hurts. I was once tapped by a practitioner who nearly drilled holes into my head and I had to physically stop them because it was so extremely unpleasant.

Considering what fine and responsive systems we are dealing with here in the form of complex meridian points and nerve junctions, it stands to reason that the "how to" of tapping with fingers on skin has a lot to do with how effective the treatment is.

To Tap Or Not To Tap?

There are, of course, alternatives to tapping. In Touch & Breathe, you just hold the points (here, once more, is the issue of how hard you push down or what "holding" means to an individual).

I personally like to gently and lightly massage the points with a single fingertip in a very small circular movement. There is a technique called Tellington TTouch where acupressure points are stimulated by sliding the skin over the point first in a full circle (from 12 o'clock to 12 o'clock) and then and without releasing the light pressure that holds the skin steady, back to the 6 o'clock position. Try it for yourself, it is an interesting effect.

Stroking downwards as though you were removing a small stain is another movement that is nice and stimulates the area in an unusual way.

The non-percussive, more massage orientated ways of stimulating the points is a good alternative on "painful points" where tapping is actually rather uncomfortable, or when the points appear to be very sore.

Young children and people who have been traumatised, for example by being hit in the face, can also feel much happier when the points are stroked gently or lightly massaged instead.

In cases of headaches, toothaches or any other type of pain that is made worse by the application of percussive beats, these are the only possible choice.

"Percussing"

We usually nowadays talk of tapping, but when the techniques were first invented, it was called "percussing" on the points.

The reason for this phrase was that the tapping movement has a fast "touch - release" pulse to it, like one would tap on a drum to make it ring out.

This is a particular movement because if you "follow through" too much with your original tap or impact, it deadens the resonance response and in the case of a drum, the sound is dull and stops dead after the impact.

In order to allow the drum to resonate, a pulse has to be swiftly put in and then the pressure removed so the drum's skin may resonate and vibrate backwards and forwards to make the sound.

Resonance

This is similar to the effects of tapping - the most responses are received when the tapper knows how to do the swift "tap and release" movement.

In trainings, I sometimes have practitioners practise this on any object that serves like a drum to find the exact type of movement that gives the most resonance and doesn't "deaden the instrument".

Pulse and Rhythm

Many times, people tap themselves and nothing seems to happen; yet when a friend or a practitioner takes over the tapping for them, with the self same opening statement, often the shift we are looking to create does occur.

I have noticed in other areas that people have *one preferred rhythm* which they will produce under many different circumstances time and time and again - whilst walking, dancing, breathing, in repetitive tasks of work and often also reflected in their choice of music.

It would be interesting to speculate that when they tap in that self same rhythm as they would naturally do, a sameness to the already existing conditions makes it less effective.

Unless you tell people to try some different rhythms, they will usually fall back on the "one and only" preferred type of pulse that generally pervades them.

There are a number of ways to try different tapping rhythms. One would be to just speed up and slow down, but more interesting rhythms develop when one considers for example, a popular or well known song that "matches the problem" and applies that rhythm to the opening statement.

Non-rhythmical tapping is another interesting possibility to unstick stuck states (i.e. problems or opening statements that have been addressed many times but nothing seems to happen). It is actually quite difficult to not fall back into one's preferred rhythm and that in and of itself adds a new dimension and new possibilities as established, old patterns are being challenged with a "new rhythm".

Echo Pulses

Try different types of strength, rhythms (from a woodpecker beat to a slow, steady heartbeat and the range in between) and also what I call "echo pulses" where you give one tap and wait for all reverberation to have ceased, then place another pulse after it. This gives a particular rhythm which is usually completely different and entirely dependent on the opening statement or issue you're currently working with.

In conclusion, I would encourage anyone who uses tapping therapies to play with all the aspects of stimulating the meridian points and to especially notice what people are actually doing as well as noticing how making changes in "the way you tap" affects the outcome of the treatment.

Tapping Therapeutically

A practitioner makes generally a choice between watching a client tap themselves and guiding them to the correct points or tapping on the client themselves.

Self Tapping

If you have not had experience of conducting the tapping part of an EFT session with another, here is the basic protocol on how to proceed:

1. Show and explain the points and at the same time as you touch the points, have the client touch the points.

2. Encourage the client to tap the points and give them feedback on the strength/speed/rhythm of their tapping, whilst mirror guiding them by moving through the points yourself so they can see what they have to do.

3. When you get into the actual treatment phase, tap with the client and once again, be a leading mirror so they can keep their mind firmly on the topic and not need to worry about where the next point is.

This of course doubles the intervention - you are proxy tapping and adding your intention/energy at the same time, and possibly releasing your own similar problems as well!

There are many times when it is essential that you should take over the tapping for the client if this is at all feasible within the restrictions of your local laws and practice set up.

Practitioner Assisted EFT

The practitioner tapping on the client becomes the only choice when:

- The client is too distressed to tap themselves;
- The client is tapping themselves ineffectually or wrongly too soft or too hard;
- The client is getting distressed because they're not sure they're doing it right or completely misses the points in spite of being shown repeatedly;

- When your intuition is telling you they are sabotaging the process;

- Nothing shifts and nothing happens when the client is tapping themselves.

Safety Rules For Tapping Another

Firstly, and before we jump on any client at all, the safety rules for "tapping another".

1. Be sure to be aware of your local legal conventions relating to touching another person in a therapeutic session. There are places on Earth where a therapist is by law forbidden to ever touch a client. You may need to adjust what you call your profession or services to be able to do therapeutic tapping at all.

2. Make sure you use some antiseptic wipes to clean your hands before touching a client. One of the tapping points is right under the client's nose and it is a disconcerting experience to smell things on the therapist's fingers.

3. ASK THE CLIENT if it would be acceptable for you to touch/tap them before you go within three feet of them! I cannot stress this one enough. Remember this. It is essential for your and your client's safety in every way.

4. Really make sure you switch your "behavioural reality check" systems to full strength. Watch your client for any signs of discomfort and adjust your normal tapping strength with that feedback you're getting. I have been the most unfortunate recipient of (half) a tapping session with a practitioner who seemed dead set on drilling holes straight through my skull and I can tell you honestly that it did nothing for either the process, or my feelings about the procedure.

The Therapeutic Tapping Pattern

Now, with the safety warnings out of the way, here's how to tap therapeutically so it works well for both you and your client.

1. Take up a comfortable position that is not too close to your client and at a 90' angle. Move in slowly and don't distort their auras with your energy field - allow yourself to mesh gently.

2. Hold out your hand to the client and let them place their hand in yours. This is a gentle and natural way to begin a physical approach and side steps instinctive flinch back responses that occur when someone with an outstretched finger tip heads straight for your head!

3. Hold the client's hand for a moment, lightly and gently, to get them accustomed to your feel and presence and touch. You can speak about the treatment some more at that point, ask them to focus on the problem - keep the conversation going until you can feel their hand relax in yours. Don't start before that has occurred - you might still get reasonable results but there is no need for making barriers to the treatment for the sake of a few more moments of acclimatisation.

4. Use the Karate Chop point for the PR treatment and NEVER poke about in other people's chests. It is horrid and you know how painful the "sore spot" can be sometimes. We're not here to cause more pain and suffering and we do NOT want our clients to link our touch with pain, ever. If you absolutely have to have the Sore Spot, then just place a flat hand over that area and soften it with the warmth from your hand instead of tapping.

5. Be careful with the under arm point, especially if you are a male with female clients. Women are protective of their breast areas and choosy about who gets to touch them there. If you note sincere resistance, it is better to leave that point out altogether or to just place your whole flat hand steadily on the general area rather than tapping.

6. If necessary, transfer the client's hand and keep holding it all through the tapping you do on them. This closes an energetic circuit, keeps the client firmly connected to you, gives them a safety anchor and sense of being supported, and can also give you the opportunity to gently massage the Gamut point or just give a supportive squeeze now and then.

7. Remind the client to breathe deeply as you tap them and remind them of the opening statement softly and gently if necessary.

8. When the treatment round is complete, de-mesh from the client gently once more. Squeeze their hand one more time lightly, gently let them go

and gently move back away from them a little to give them room to establish their perception of their energy systems without interference from yours at a close range.

If you have not done this before, find a willing human - friend or family member - to try out the gentle approach described.

Ask their feedback on what it felt like to them and if you can, have them do the same to you.

You don't need to do an entire sequence for this exercise; the important points are that you practise and heighten your awareness of the gentle meshing/de-meshing at the start and end of the treatment and what it feels like to keep the closed circuit whilst holding the client's hand.

If your willing human is willing, experiment with the difference between this and just tapping someone without the hand holding and the meshing/de-meshing rituals.

You will notice a dramatic difference in rapport, and the client's comfort, sense of safety and relaxation.

More Therapy Tapping Patterns

This chapter represents an overview of the variations in which EFT can be administered, received, performed and used in the treatment flow.

Self Tapping, Classic EFT– Client Tapping Themselves, Full Round

This is the base technique and in work with clients is performed specifically when the outcome of the session is that the client should learn EFT itself rather than being treated for something specific. In its purest form it is actually rarely done like this outside workshops and trainings.

Self Tapping, Therapist Led – Client tapping themselves, following the therapist's lead who is showing them the points on themselves.

Here, the therapist (or counsellor, helper, healer etc) touches the points on themselves and the client taps the points the therapist has indicated. This version is used when the client cannot be touched; when the client is still learning EFT and for intuitive tapping, i.e. the therapist intuiting an order and sequence of tapping points which may be different from the normal, classic EFT round.

Double Tapping – Client and therapist tapping together a full round on a pre-arranged opening statement and reminder phrase.

Not to be confused with the version whereby the therapist is leading the round and the client simply following, in the "double tapping" event both work together as equals and align their intention to a third entity, namely the problem or disturbance in question (think of it as singing together). This activity creates quite a powerful pledge field and also, creates deep state alignment in both parties and following, deep rapport.

As both need to sing the same song, this has to be either a full classic EFT round or alternatively, a pre-arranged short cut or personalised sequence of points.

Therapeutic Tapping – Therapist taps on the client.

We have already discussed this in detail; here I would like to simply note that this tapping pattern particularly helps the therapist develop a real sense of understanding a client's energy system, their needs and also and very importantly, their own responses and reactions to engaging with clients and their energy systems.

Interim Tapping – Client and/or therapist tapping outside of set rounds of classic EFT.

Many therapists quickly discover that it is a great time saver as well as making the general treatment flow more elegant when either client, therapist or both just keep on tapping after a major round with a set up, for example whilst discussing aspects, insights or what should come along next. Mostly, this is done intuitively led by the therapist who advises or demonstrates to the client which points to tap on whilst the discussion is taking place.

This also allows for other variations on the basic theme, for example tapping a single point repeatedly for a much longer period of time; holding a point all through a particular part of a discussion; rapidly switching from one side to the other with bi-lateral points etc.

Proxy Tapping – Therapist tapping in the place of the client for the client's problem and with the client's opening statements.

This can be of use when the client needs to be quiet, is overwhelmed, too tired to tap themselves and generally, whenever a therapist's intuition suggests this might be a good idea.

Harmonic Tapping – Therapist tapping different points as the client taps classic EFT or a pre-arranged personalised algorithm

This is an interesting and quite advanced version of the double tapping pattern which can happen spontaneously when therapist and client are in rapport. A simpler version is to "echo" the point the client last tapped on and as they are already moving on to the next.

These patterns are just some of what can happen spontaneously in the seemingly simple act of two people tapping on meridian points whilst aligning in their intention to unblock, heal and restore the energy system of the client. I invite you to pay attention to the many different variations on this simple theme as they arise in direct, intuitive response to the energetic occurrences in the treatments.

Creating & Using EFT Short Cuts

For problems that have a habit of recurring or being triggered by the environment repeatedly, as is the case with addictions and sometimes allergies, or problems that have been around for a long time and have an "entrainment aspect", using shortened sequences of special points (or algorithms) can be very useful as they are more specific to the problem, as well as being quicker to do than a full round of EFT for example.

Making a Custom Algorithm

This first set is based on using some form of Kinesiology in order to ascertain the order and sequence of the special points for the custom algorithm or short cut sequence.

1. Think of or state out loud what it's going to be for (insomnia, depression, general miserableness etc).

2. Find some form of self Kinesiology testing such as using a pendulum, muscle test etc. Calibrate for a "yes - no" or "strong - weak" response.*

3. Touch in turn all of the points you wish to include with one finger and test them with the other hand.

   a) if it tests yes or strong, move on.

   b) if it tests no or weak, write down the point or remember it.

4. When you have all the relevant points, ask, should this be treated first? and go through only the relevant ones you found in 3) until you have established the first point of your custom sequence.

5. For the remaining points, ask, should this be treated second? Repeat until you have established the correct order and sequence by a simple process of elimination.

If you want a custom algorithm for something that troubles you regularly and often, you might also like to have a "one point stop point" or "emergency stop point".

6. Touch your sequence points one after the other with the question, if I want to use only one, is this the one? to discover which one that is.

Short Cuts & Algorithms Without Muscle Testing

It is possible to discover relevant points of a sequence by touching each point in turn.

The ones that feel "weird" or tender, sore, strange in any way make up the custom algorithm; the one point which feels the most noticeably different when touched makes the emergency stop point (see below).

Another option is to use the EmoTrance question of, "Where do you feel this problem in your body? Show me with your hands." and choose points which either have direct meridian connections to these ereas, or which are close to the EFT treatment points.

It is also possible to ask clients directly to try points and sequences of points to test which ones have the most relaxing effects. Working out these custom algorithms together with a client is a very nice experience for both as we get to pay really close attention to how the points respond to stimulation when the problem "thoughtfield" is being contacted and to experience the very real differences in relevance of the various meridians.

Lastly, the therapist may either through the medium of rapport or by using the shamanistic move **into the client's problem** in order to ascertain in their own body which points would be the ones to be most likely to bring about a change. With this approach, you do however need to be very careful not to inadvertently treat your own problems and when a sequence derived in this fashion (or any other fashion and including muscle testing!) is tested by the client, their actual reactions to the shortcut sequence is of course, the final answer as to whether or not the right algorithm has been found.

Emergency STOP

I also recommend to find a single point to be used for the emergency stop - this will be useful also in the context of addictive cravings and craving to do the addiction later on. This is used as a STOP on the threshold of the behaviour and just to give the client enough time and space to start using another protocol to relieve the problem, such as a personalised sequence or classic EFT, for example.

You would ask the client's body directly to let you know which point it should be and gently and swiftly test all the points you are working with. You usually get quite a profoundly noticeable instant weakening when you find the right point for the Emergency Stop Procedure.

Clients can be advised to use the Emergency STOP at any time and if they wish, can tap on it as often as they need throughout the day as well.

You can assign the KC point or the Sore Spot for an Emergency STOP if muscle testing is not an option with a particular client and you cannot come up with anything better through intuition or experience.

If you do that, strengthen the usage with suggestions. Further, the Emergency STOP point can then lead into a full EFT round which is useful for the client under any circumstances.

Energy "Chords"

Sometimes, combination holds of more than one point at the same time can have a "breakthrough" effect on a client's energy system.

Likely candidates for such chords can be discovered during the "EFT Channel Clearing" protocol and explored with the client.

Standard Short Cuts

Some points appear more often in algorithms and shortcuts than others. For example, the Under Eye point is nearly always a good candidate to at least "try on everything", as is the Collarbone Point.

The two points relating to psychological reversal, namely the Karate Chop Point and the Sore Spot are also something that can be tried swiftly and often have an impact, whatever the problem.

Lists of standard short cuts can be found in TFT publications if this is something you wish to explore further.

In general, and this is a fascinating aspect of the short cuts, as soon as you begin to use these, you are beginning to cross the border from what might be termed "pure EFT" treatments into really working with the meridian/energy system in the wider sense.

Working With Time Lines

With most presenting problems, it is very useful to take the time line of the problem; for some it is of the essence.

Creating a time line of the problem (or problem group) can be as simple as to ask, "When did this happen exactly?" or "When did you first notice these symptoms?" and then to follow up with the question, "What was your life like at that time?"

In some cases, however, it is useful to physically draw a time line of the problem and to write down the relevant incidences that are related. This is particularly so in cases that involve a lot of ecology considerations, primary and secondary gain as well as those that seemed to appear resistant to treatment to begin with.

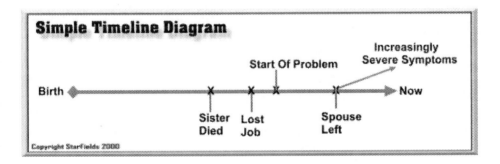

Time Line and Aspects

A time line graphic can be most useful to keep how aspects are related in consciousness for both you and the client to actually see and understand. It is an excellent way to map a problem that may have been nebulous and mysterious before. The time line graphic can also perform a number of other very useful functions in the context of treating complex or long standing issues:

Disassociation from the whole problem complex. When we do the EFT treatments themselves, we generally **want** the client to be at least partially in touch with the emotions of the problem because that seems to really help to target the stimulation of the meridian points. In the discussion or exploration parts of the treatment, disassociation or "taking the bigger picture" can be a very useful mental shift that helps the client gain a sense of at least understanding, if not the sense that control over **the whole system** of the problem might be within their grasp.

Respectful Planning. The time line map offers the possibility of real discussion with the client as to where they want to be in the treatment, what they would like to do and in which order and sequence, in a very practical way.

Structure & Guidance. Especially with the long standing problems, complex or seemingly illogical problems there can be more than one core set of causes, incidents and memories – indeed, there usually are more than one core set of systems and that is **exactly** why the problem has proven so resistant to treatment. Logically and in practise, these "problem systems" have a multitude of aspects, memories, decisions, gate keepers and so forth and to hold all of this detail in consciousness is nearly impossible. The time line map certainly helps to bring both the client and the practitioner back to the main structure when they have investigated a particular tributary, shows what and how has changed in black and white, and provides the logical next step to the treatment process.

Bridging Multi-Sessions. EFT especially tends to have the promise by presupposition that anything may be resolved in a single session. With complex problems, that might not always be the case and to keep the work on one problem system on track over a number of sessions, the time line map is most useful. It is more useful than note taking by the therapist because the client is **sharing** in the adjusting and making of this map and sees it too. It is certainly an anchor that makes it easier to remember what has gone before if there was a week in between sessions and return very much to the place where you left off previously more or less as soon as the map is produced.

Testing. As I have said many times already, testing is of the essence to really complete any treatment properly and tidily – and I mean, energetically tidily in that sense. With the many sub-components and sub-aspects of a complex systemic problem set, **each treated aspect** needs to be tested. The map simply makes sure you don't forget anything important during this process which can and of course often is, very emotionally charged and also, exciting as it unfolds.

Special Time Line Applications

A nice feature of time line work is to construct context specific overviews on certain topics (or problem groups) which serve to filter for the patterns that are inherent in these topics.

This brings the underlying patterns of the topic to conscious awareness and allows both clients and therapists (and self helpers) to track back to causative events, or to formulate opening statements which are aimed at collapsing the underlying structure all these events, manifestations and symptoms have in common.

Crime Line

Think of a time line as a person's movement through their personal history from birth to death which encompasses all their experiences and significant moments.

Now, instead of all of the significant experiences, Crime line only deals with **crimes committed by any one given individual** - note, not crimes committed against them which is a different topic altogether.

Crime line is primarily a self help tool for it is rare and far to find a therapist to whom one may tell about one's secret crimes - things that only you know about, that you may well have sought to hide from everyone including yourself, and things that you might not be able to tell a therapist because they would not understand how you could view these as "crimes" at all and may try and convince you that "it wasn't your fault" or "you were so little, you couldn't have known any better" or "you're being too hard on yourself" or even "I'm sure it wasn't as bad as all of that".

The fascinating thing about an individual's crimes is that they are extremely idiosyncratic and the judgement as to what is and what isn't a true crime must reside with the individual themselves.

For example, a grown man brought up in a strict religious community may absolutely consider the removal of an apple from a neighbour's tree without permission when he was three years old as a crime that was never discovered or punished - a crime of tremendous proportions that had serious repercussions on the man's neurology and may still have to this day.

EFT Crime Line Resolution

Here, you draw a line and note down the major crimes you know you committed during your life time. If need be or there is an aspect of that, past life Crime lines in context are also a possibility.

Mark down clearly with an X the incidents you remember most vividly and if you will, you can take different perceptional positions; for example, which are your worst crimes according to your mother, father, society, God, lovers, and in general, other-than-self.

Treat these incidents and their respective emotions with EFT, one by one, starting with the oldest first (as often older memories collapse entire gestalts that were build on their original imprints/resonances).

Continue until you have cleared the entire Crime line and have come to resolutions you personally find very satisfactory, or at least, liveable with.

Crime lines are interesting and can prove to be very valuable in the contexts of relationships, business success, self esteem and a host of other realms of an individuals' life.

Other time line applications can deal with success and failure; for example, a Glory Line, Success Line and/or a Love Line can provide breakthrough sessions, insights, and major changes in a person's self construct.

Finding The Perfect Opening Statements

As every EFT practitioner knows, the exact words spoken in the exact order and sequence in the set up as the opening statements and/or reminder phrases have everything to do with how successful the entire treatment round becomes.

It is essential not to filter what a person says or to put a different spin on it by accident; this might mean that the real problem cannot be resolved at all. Therefore, the prime directive of formulating opening statements is that they must be in the client's own words and that ONLY the client can know the right words to say.

In this chapter, we are going to take a closer look at the main linguistic structures employed to elicit or recognise the most powerful opening statements which will lead directly to a major shift on the problem in hand.

Physiological & Tonal Markers

The most commonly used and most profoundly useful of all the many ways to find those magic words is to listen carefully to what the client says and to observe the client with every sense at your disposal. Phrases, sentences or even single words which point the way to a major underlying energy disturbance are marked out clearly, even in the most controlled person, in many different ways.

Here is a brief reminder of the main markers. Any disturbances in the energy body and especially, severe disturbances will become manifest in changes here:

Movement

- facial expressions
- gestures
- head/neck
- eyes
- hands
- feet
- shoulders

Skin

- colour
- tone
- temperature

Breathing

- where from?
- how deep?
- regularity/irregularities

Voice

- tone
- volume
- pitch
- wave shape

It is important to remember that fluctuations in these noticeable presentations of a human body are based on disturbances in the energy system; and of course, experienced EFT practitioners will be able to feel the energy of any given sentence a client will say, any given situation they are describing. After a while, there is no conscious effort needed to know exactly what to tap on, and to know where to tap for it (see also the Healer Model).

Languaging Patterns For Opening Statements

Connective Strings With Conjunctions

Oftentimes, the client names problems which appear to have no discernible emotional charge for a number of reasons. Using conjunctions instead of further questions allows the client to move in closer to the central problem in stages, without suggesting anything or putting your own words into the clients mouth.

There are the coordinating conjunctions in English, also known as the **FANBOYS**: For-And-Nor-But-Or-Yet-So, and the subordinating conjunctions (sometimes called a dependent word or subordinator) which establish the relationship between the dependent clause and the rest of the sentence. These also turn the clause into something that depends on the rest of the sentence for its meaning.

after	if	though
although	if only	till
as	in order that	unless
as if	now that	until
as long as	once	where
as though	rather than	whereas
because	since	wherever
before	so that	while
even if	than	when
even though	that	whenever

Example:

"I can't relate with my husband"

"and ...?"

"And it is getting me down."

"because ...?"

"I feel I don't love him anymore."

"and ...?"

"That makes me terribly sad."

The use of simple conjunctions establishes a flow beyond the ordinary thoughts which block off just as meridians do at a certain point, because if we went any further, it would hurt too much.

This languaging technique is very powerful but whether or not a client will actually allow themselves to go beyond the original statement and into the real energetic injuries beyond using the conjunctions depends heavily on whether they trust the therapist enough to keep them safe.

Resolving Conflicts – Merging Conflicting Thoughtfields

Since its first inception, this pattern has been modelled and used in various ways by many because it is so very useful.

Often, problems do not derive from one thing or another, but from a combination of seemingly irreconcilable thoughts, values, goals, gestalts – thoughtfields, if you will.

After years of struggling with publishers in one form or the other, one day I stood in the kitchen and shouted, "Goddamn it, I HATE publishers. But I want to get Adventures published! Aaargh!"

This original incident was very useful because in truth, hating publishers is not a particular problem if you work in ship building. But as an author who wants to get their book published, it really does represent a serious problem because of the tension between the two.

Linking up two, three or more conflicting thoughtfields in a single opening statement and reminder phrase goes directly to the tension between them and changes all of them in the process which makes this a particularly useful and time saving device in EFT treatments.

Any of the conjunctions above may be used to language the opening statement in this way. (*See also Needs & Wants*).

Affirmations & Goal Statements

It is important to remember that EFT functionally increases and/or restores flow in the energy body.

As such, EFT does not install anything new that wasn't there before and this is important to remember at all times, but most especially when dealing with goal setting and varieties thereof, such as affirmations.

There is no such thing as "rubbing in positives" during an EFT treatment and this is not how the actual **emergence of positive results** comes into being.

Simply put, humans are capable of the most astonishing feats once they are fit and healthy in body and in mind.

This is not some form of religious delusion or wishful thinking but simply **a structural reality** for any human who does not suffer from material damage to their systems (i.e. genetic problems, brain damage following an accident).

What EFT does is to get the blockages out of the way which allow the **natural abilities, functions and actualities of achievement** inherent in the person who are using this to shine through and become activated.

For example, if someone would like to become more prosperous and was to use the affirmation of, "I am prosperous and I deeply and profoundly love and accept myself", no special angel comes down from heaven and waves a magic wand.

Instead, they will be addressing their reversals, reservations, fears and blockages on the topic and set themselves free from the contortions which precluded access to the simple human ability to seek out prosperity and to manage it successfully once it has been achieved – and that is something everyone is born with.

It is true that this is a little to complex or difficult to accept for some clients and there is no harm in using the metaphor of "rubbing in positives" in some cases; in many others, the idea that they already have what they need to succeed and heal and it is simply a question of releasing the blockages and bonds which hold them back is actually a very generative and healing pre-supposition.

Example "Goal Setting" Statements

Affirmation Phrasing (positive, first person, present tense):

I am prosperous.

When used with EFT, these classical affirmations can be a double edged sword. For example, if a person with the goal to loose weight uses this set up with EFT on topics such as, "I am beautiful", "I am perfect" etc. what happens is not that they lose weight but they **stop worrying about being overweight** instead. In the long term, this is certainly a very good thing but in the short term can lead clients to reject further EFT treatments on the grounds that they just end up being happy right where they are and no changes are made. The fact that often problems rather than being solved as expected simply cease to exist as the idea of a problem instead is a fascinating aspect of EFT treatments and should be born in mind, especially where health issues are a pressing concern.

Wishing Well Phrasing (hoping, wishing, etc):

I wish I was prosperous.

This is quite a different form of positive phrasing and one that may precede a full standard affirmation by a long time. In many instances, to be able to allow oneself a round of EFT to even wish for something which may have been entirely out of reach for a lifetime is a major turning point. It means that the individual is at **least allowing themselves the possibility** of this something to enter their worlds and a very powerful and magical form of energy is the result that can become a positive force for change.

Desire Phrasing (desiring, longing, wanting, etc)

I long for prosperity.

Not all emotions are bad and must be tapped away forthwith. Positive, clean emotions of desire are an extraordinary motivator **towards** a goal, aim, target or desired state of being, creating a kind of energetic river flow **towards** the desired state. This is very helpful to make it easier for an individual to reach their dreams as they can go with their own flow.

Free Will Phrasing (will, choose, decide, etc)

I choose prosperity.

To direct ones own energy system absolutely towards an outcome of any kind, a state of congruency is of the essence – no doubt left, no fears to overcome and it is all forward movement where will has become aligned with the energetic flow of desire. This is a very powerful state of being indeed and when a person reaches this state, they become basically unstoppable.

Consequences Phrasing (accepting, owning, having, holding etc)

I accept prosperity.

This phrasing clears up remaining doubts as to the question if the individual can handle what they have asked for – an important principle in magic, as it is in all-you-can-eat restaurants.

Aspects come to awareness in this phrasing which were not apparent before because this is about living with the change having being made, with the goal having being reached AFTER that moment of achievement. This is actually very important because with goals of any kind, mostly we don't tend to think any further than reaching it – the goal becomes all there is and there is no life beyond.

The consequences phrasing is therefore also a device which connects the current actions, the goal and then the **life beyond** in a flowing and ecological fashion.

Working With Trance States

Clients in EFT treatments enter trance states of various depths naturally and as a result of engaging in energy work.

A "trance" state is a shift into an **energetic state of being** that affects the totality (physicality, psychology, energy body etc) entirely.

What is sometimes mis-named as "ordinary waking awareness" is only another state of being, existing in a narrow range for most people which they inhabit for whatever reasons.

The thing is that the energy body changes quite dramatically at different states of being – you could think of it in terms of a "normally" depressed person who falls in love for the first time and becomes literally unrecognisable to themselves and others, in the way they think, feel, act and even look.

In the most commonly inhabited narrow range of totality states, the most confusion, chaos and weirdness exists in the way of shields, blockages, disturbances, foreign thoughtfields (such as "evil CDs") and everyday accumulations of clutter of one kind or the other.

In hypnosis, for example, the practitioner seeks to create a state shift to a different state of being where the energy body is much less disturbed, where there is much less going on, where the shields are down and where suggestions (CDs) will enter into the energy body and remain there permanently.

In repetitive behaviour addictions, the person shifts state into a state of being where the thoughtfields and disturbances which would ordinarily plague them and make their lives hell simply cease to exist.

As soon as you as a person to think of a problem and then start to tap, they enter totality states which are different and other than their "ordinary awareness" states and resemble classical hypnosis states quite perfectly.

Whilst the clients are in a trance state, they are vulnerable to "post hypnotic suggestions" by the practitioner and in general, open to all kinds of effects and influences from which they would ordinarily find themselves shielded and protected – for the good or bad, it matters not.

The point is that I believe it to be of the essence that healers, practitioners and even self help users of all the METs and definitely including EFT should:

- Understand the basics of trance states and trance processes;

- Be aware at all time of the depth of trance in their clients;

- Know enough so they will not prejudice the client's processes by installing their own ideas, issues etc.;

- Know enough about the principles of suggestion and state to be able to protect and safeguard their clients when they are incapable of protecting themselves in the open trance states.

I would make the comment that trance states are not restricted to the well known relaxation and sleepiness states which are commonly used in technical hypnotherapy.

In effect **any** state that is outside the narrow range of ordinary states for an individual will have the same non-protection and clarity aspects to it, including very high energy states of euphoria, ecstasy and excitement. These types of states are regularly utilised to install "post hypnotic suggestions" in political rallies, religious cults and the "Hey Ho!" types schools of personal development seminars.

I am making this note because of course, energy treatments can and do induce euphoric states in the clients; and even if a practitioner for reasons best known to themselves refuses the opportunity to install something positive when trance states present themselves, at least they should be very careful what they say and how they say it so they don't install degenerative thoughtfields in the client by accident.

For simplicity, I have named the euphoric trance states "Up Trances" and the relaxed trance states "Down Trances".

First, here are some markers which will let you notice both because they are structurally the same:

Trance State Markers – All Trance States

- A sense of deep rapport – the client is "wide open and receptive"
- A definite sense of energy shift – the client is other or different from when they came in and were talking from their ordinary states of being.
- A definite change in their thinking – the client says or expresses ideas, opinions, insights which are indications that they are thinking very differently from how they normally think;
- A definite change in physiology – the client acts and physically looks differently from their base state.

Up Trance Markers

- Focus of attention way outside of self – "Oh isn't this world beautiful!"
- Bright, excited energy
- Fast movements, speech, movements up to a point of epiphany where everything just falls silent and reverent;
- Expressing energy by getting up, singing, dancing, being unable to sit still.
- Skin flushed, warm, "glowing"; movements unrestricted and spontaneous.

Down Trance Markers

- Focus of attention on internal processes rather than "real world stimuli".
- Relaxation of body and facial muscles, breathing more deeply than usual, moving slower.
- Slightly unfocussed look in the eyes, skin tone a little paler than usual.
- Slight lag between stimulus (input) and response (reaction) - the deeper the trance, the more noticeable this becomes.
- Unconscious and reflexive responses rather than controlled, planned, conscious thought, speech and action.

Trance Language & Internal Representations

Here are the essential points about trance, internal representations and language in brief. For more detailed information, please look into NLP-Hypnosis training (rather than the older forms of classical hypnosis).

- The deeper the trance, the more literally any suggestion will be processed AND the more powerful and real a client's internal representations will become.

- Internal representations cannot process a negative - "Don't think of a blue tree" produces an internal representation of a blue tree. Similarly, "Don't worry" produces an internal representation of worry. If relaxation is required rather than worrying, the phrasing in trance must be, "Please relax." instead.

- Trance Language must be carefully supervised to not accidentally install damaging suggestions.

- Example: "Don't think that it is going to get much worse, and don't be terrified that you're going to die, all alone, in misery and terrible pain." installs very negative internal representations and in a trance state, the client will not only **be there**, dying alone and in agony, but **feel it** AND may template it, i.e. create a template goal out of it and make it come true.

- Practitioners who work with clients in trance states MUST train themselves to make beneficial internal representations for their clients with the words they use. Please note that in EFT we work with negatives a lot because we use them for the opening statements to lead us to the source of the energetic injury which we seek to heal; this makes it doubly important for the practitioner to know just when we are using an opening statement and we are healing it, and when we are "just chatting" or "making comments" which may well slip into the client's "unconscious mind" (aka those other states of being that are always present but not always, rarely or virtually never accessed in consciousness).

- Beneficial suggestions can speed and smooth the client's experience of the treatment itself and be used to support the client's healing processes. For example, it is always good to suggest to a client that they will notice the benefits of the treatment and how whatever they are doing or wanting will continue to increase, improve, flower and grow, become easier to have, be and do – etc.

Here are a number of other essential points about trance states in EFT treatments in brief. In truth, this topic would require an entire book in its own right as it is so little known outside the hypnosis communities and yet so deeply essential in all treatments of human beings when trance states are even a possibility.

Trance states can be induced by the practitioner themselves going into trance **if** the client is in rapport. If you are unused to being aware of state shifts in yourself and others, try this simple exercise.

Close your eyes, breathe deeply and allow yourself to relax down on the outbreath, a little more with each outbreath, letting gravity help you along. Notice how your experience of your body changes, how your experience of sensory input changes and how indeed, your energy changes as you do this. Now, reverse the breathing pattern and "lift" on each inbreath until you have re-gained your "ordinary" totality state. That was a down trance.

For the up trance, breathe deeply but just slightly more rapidly than you usually do and focus on a sense of rising on the inbreath. Look around wide-eyed as you do this, continuing to breathe deeply, straighten and try and get the sense that you are about to take off with the energy that is building up and up.

Slowly dissolve the state as before by breathing more slowly and step back down to your "ordinary" totality state.

With a little practise and with paying some attention as to where you are in this scale of up – normal – down state shifts, you will build up an unconscious awareness of where you are and where your client is at any given point in the treatment flow. More importantly, you will be able to use these deliberate state shifts in yourself to help the client reach a place where they are most likely able to do the work they need to do in a session to heal what needs to be healed.

An important aspect of being able to control one's own states of being at least is that one does not accidentally create a state mismatch with the client and thereby profoundly and painfully, shatters rapport in an instant.

To put it simply, a loud, high, happy squawk from a therapist going to a client who is processing something important in a down trance state is the equivalent of getting an electric shock – not a pleasant sensation as you can imagine as well as being most counter-productive to the client and their processes.

However, should a client be stuck in a down trance and it wasn't possible to reach them or to get them out, a high, loud squawk might be exactly what is required to "get the client back" and have the session proceed successfully once more.

In this context, we can also re-visit the idea of having the client be in a "stable state" before they leave the office. There is quite a bit on this topic in various chapters of this book already; here once again, I would point out how extremely helpful it is to not only recognise existing states but also to develop the ability to shift states in yourself and in your client with ease and confidence.

Metaphor In EFT Treatments

This is a centrally important section from "Adventures In EFT" that I have deliberately once more included in this book on the advanced patterns of EFT. In my opinion, there **is** nothing more advanced than an understanding of the nature and structure of metaphor as a carrier for energy and although of course the basic metaphor EFT protocols are a fun tool, there is far, far more to it than that.

The word metaphor means "an amphora that carries a lot of things inside". Well, they carry thoughtfields in our case, and in many cases are the only connection we can possibly have with disturbances in the energy system which are beyond, above, beneath and other-dimensional than what we can talk about in the labels of our ordinary speech.

If you are serious about deep healing in quantum realms; really learning how to understand the laws of nature which are very different from those governing the "physical" universe; and really want to be able to perform the multidimensional computations which are indeed, of the essence in true energy work, be it with EFT or any other modality, then familiarity with metaphor work is simply of the essence.

The only way to understand energy and metaphor is to **do it**. To use metaphor elicitations with others, with yourself and to try it out for yourself, learning in the way that children learn about the nature of the universe, by trial and error, until an understanding begins to build in your mind.

I highly recommend this for all, be they absolute technicians who pride themselves on their Spock-like knowledge and systems computations or be they absolutely holistically minded and wish to work with nothing but their heart and intuition.

Energy healing is multi-dimensional in nature, and EFT **is** energy healing, make no mistake about it. It is in these multi-dimensional matrices that we all need to learn to work, physicists and Reiki healers alike, and there is no teacher or teaching system more profound, more useful, more user friendly or more astonishing in its repercussions than metaphor work.

So, and now with this acclamation and introduction in place, let us turn to the topic of this chapter, which is ...

An Introduction To Using Metaphor In Energy Therapies

One of the most powerful forms of communication possible lies at the threshold between conscious awareness and the realms of the unseen - the metaphor.

Not a linguistic construct, not a highbrow nominalisation, but a shortcut phrase to describe an incredibly beautiful and complex function of our neurology, metaphors truly and literally "reach the parts that no other words can reach".

In the quest of "getting in touch" with your own or a client's unique internal experiences of any given problem, metaphors are probably the single most powerful, infinitely subtle and precise forms of linking up that are known to us at this point.

If you think of any given problem as a localised disturbance at the energetic level, and we wish to re-balance this disturbance and return it to Even Flow, the key task is to make contact with that disturbance, to reach it somehow, because only if we can reach and touch it, can we change and heal it.

In EFT for example, the "opening statement" performs the function of this link up to the disturbance; but every energy therapy has by needs the link up performed in some way, even if it is only the client thinking about the problem in question.

How Can You Describe A Love?

We have certain generic labels for emotions - love, hate, panic, distress. There's quite a few of them but it is important to always remember that:

Firstly, your love is NOT my love and your hate is NOT like mine. Any one single persons individual experience is absolutely unique and totally idiosyncratic. If I have learned anything in the last 25 years, it is that simple fact.

The same holds true for any other form of pain and suffering. My toothache is inherently different from your toothache, even if the exact same tooth was damaged in the exact same way which in and of itself, is a structural impossibility.

To begin to communicate about such internal experiences at all, and have a hope that at least a resonance or gentle echo travels across to another, we label these experiences, best we can.

The more intense and/or disturbing these experiences become, the less possibility exists to still use the "off the shelf" categories of words to try and explain, even to yourself, what is going on inside. It is then people turn automatically to metaphor.

For energy psychologists and users of meridian therapies, this is a wonderful gift. Metaphors are in many instances, absolutely the keys to unlocking the door behind which the disturbance lies, and in many instances, they are about the only key that will fit that particular door.

But metaphors are much more than that, of course.

They are the bridges between sensations and emotions and conscious awareness; they also bridge unconscious awareness to conscious awareness, such as would be in the case of so called "repressed" memories or incidences that were simply forgotten, or that were causative to the genesis of a disturbance yet consciously, we do not know about the cause and effect involved.

Spontaneously Occurring Metaphors

In general treatment with clients, or with the self, metaphors that occur naturally and spontaneously should always, always be listened to and treated with the greatest respect.

When someone thinks or says that a problem is "like a huge weight on my shoulders" or that they feel as though they were "drowning in sorrow", it is not just a poetic turn of phrase that would be better served with a more sensible expression. What you are looking at when metaphors are expressed is a cohesive energetic system that contains many separate components within it, delivered to you for the resolution right there on a platter so a superior and highly ecological solution can be found.

How wonderfully complex and rich metaphors really are, and how many levels of meaning and being they encompass is hard to put in linear words. However, here is a simple example. One lady could not speak up for herself to anyone in authority and never in front of a group of people.

She said her throat would begin to feel scratchy, as though "a piece of holly was stuck in there". In this case, it was an EFT treatment and the holly sensation turned into the first opening statement. After a number of rounds and some talking in between, a causative memory emerged of being terrified of Santa as a child, being unable to speak up and say what she wanted for Christmas. At the time, she had had a cold and her mother excused her on the grounds of this and took her out of the situation.

Consider, for a moment, how amazing that is. Fifty years later, the lady describes the pain in her throat in terms of "holly", something that in the UK is absolutely associated with Christmas and nothing much beside. The metaphor did not only pertain to the absolute sensation, locked in all that time ago, of both having a sore throat and being terrified to speak out loud, but also told us already of the causative incident, showed how very well remembered it was even though it had been consciously forgotten, and gave us the very key that would unlock the problem at last.

Consider also, if you will, how much harder it would have been to find the causative incident and to really repair the energetic injury caused way back then and locked right into the structure of the client's energetic systems without the guidance of the holly metaphor. Following the treatment, the sensation never recurred and the speaking-up problem never came back in that form.

Eliciting Metaphors

As metaphors are such a superb system to guide us towards the right intervention points, as well as allowing the client or the self to express sensations, emotions and states of being in a deeply personal and meaningful fashion, the act of helping someone name their problem in a metaphorical way is a most useful intervention from many angles.

There are many ways in which a metaphor for a problem may be elicited. The simplest way of conversational metaphor elicitation is simply to ask, "So what is this pain like?"

Your intuition may well begin to twitch and stir when answers come such as, "Ah it's like someone is beating me constantly in the back, with every breath I take." - "Like I've been stabbed in the back" - "Like something is cutting away at me" - "Like there's something pushing down hard on my stomach" and other examples of this nature.

But whatever the answer may be, and whether or not you can sense just how this particular metaphor had been chosen and not any other from a million different possibilities, using the client's very words for opening statements or treatment points is profoundly effective, as well as often profoundly moving.

A different approach to eliciting a metaphor is to ask, "If this pain had a colour, what would it be? If you knew what size it was, how big would it be? If it had a shape, a weight, what could those be?" That can be quite enough to do a treatment most successfully - "Even though I have this big grey green block on my heart, I deeply and profoundly love and accept myself."

Sometimes, one could go one step further and ask directly at this point, "And what does this big grey green block remind you of?"

This example actually happened, and the answer to the question was, "It reminds me of my brother's Wellington boots when he stood on my chest that day."

It is interesting to note that metaphor can be expressed behaviourally just as well as through speech. When you ask someone how big a pain is, or where it is, what shape it is, and so forth, they will show you with their hands, in fact they will be painting an existing energetic reality for you into the room so you can see it, too.

Making Real Changes Visible

Metaphors are not only for the beginning part of the treatment to find an entrance point to the problem; not only for the middle part of a treatment to deal with the problem directly, they are also a superb feedback mechanism and testing device.

The holly in the throat, for example, did not disappear on the first round of treatment but it shrank and moved slightly lower instead. If we consider the holly to be a description of a real energetic injury, we can track the effectiveness of our treatments most precisely through the changes in the metaphorical representation or interface.

Someone who showed with their hands how big and wide a pain was and where it was located upon asking, can show you with the precision of a tape measure just how much repair was accomplished during the treatment. This, by the way, is an excellent device to use with children and those who have difficulties with words in general - "Show me where the pain is, show me how big it is." - before, and after the treatment.

To sum up:

Metaphors are not an esoteric past-time but a highly sophisticated, extremely powerful interface device that is easy to use if it is treated respectfully and within its own context.

Metaphor elicitation is a very useful treatment strategy under many circumstances, from using the swiftness of their targeting to take you to the core of the problem, to sometimes being the only way into a problem in the first place, especially if the problem is highly repressed or has resisted treatment in the normal way to begin with.

Switching to metaphor elicitation when the treatment seems to get stuck or go nowhere is extremely helpful and provides the breakthrough in many instances where nothing else would or could have worked.

Using the client's own natural metaphors is the fastest and easiest way to resolving existing problems known to mankind. Listen with great care for the verbal markers and watch with similar care to the behavioural descriptions and use what you have learned.

Metaphors represent a very accurate, client driven feedback device that is perfect for testing and monitoring the changes that are occurring during and after the treatment.

Metaphorically based energy therapy interventions are extremely ecological and holistic because they bring together both the conscious and the unconscious awareness of any given problem in its totality - as an actual physical manifestation as well as its energetic dimensions.

Metaphor Elicitation

General metaphors can be elicited with the question.

- "What is this problem like?"

- "What is it like to feel this way?"

- "What is it like to have this problem/to live with this problem?"

You can elicit details with questions such as:

- "If your pain/problem had a size, what would it be?"

- "If your pain/ problem had a texture/ colour/ weight/ shape/ scent/ density/ etc, what would it be?"

Repeating the words the client used to answer in order to build up the metaphor, you add up what they said for each question:

So your pain is this big, spiky, hard, heavy, dense, black, smells of iron, is of a longish shape - what would that remind you of?"

Then the metaphor materialises and the client might say: "It's a sword, an old black pitted sword that's stuck in my stomach." What we now have is an existing energetic reality, manifest, named and open to all kinds of interaction and intervention.

In the example above, you can just tap on the manifest metaphor and see what turns up. Often, "real" memories emerge that may be treated with the story protocol; at other times the metaphor changes and fluxes as you do the treatments with the client.

Another option is to discuss the client's relationship with the metaphor. In the example, the client experienced "a real sense of dread, stomach churning fear" when confronted with the metaphorical object manifest.

Problems and solutions can be discussed. We have a client with a sword stuck in their stomach - can it be removed? What would happen if we did that?

Metaphorical ecology discussions are very interesting because we are not talking about issues that are emotionally and intellectually over clouded such as, "My husband doesn't take care of me."

Advanced Aspects

Often, when a SUDs reading is being undertaken, **more than one** number comes to mind. This is a perfect example of the issue having more than one component to it, more than one strand or, in EFT terminology, more than one aspect.

Especially when dealing with complex presenting problems, "gestalts" of problems and issues such as high level nominalisations of identity or global collections of many memories pertaining to a single topic (such as "mother", "money", "self esteem" and so forth), but also when dealing with a single trauma that may have only lasted for a second, you might find that there are many different aspects that are important in the context of the whole.

Mapping Aspects Successfully

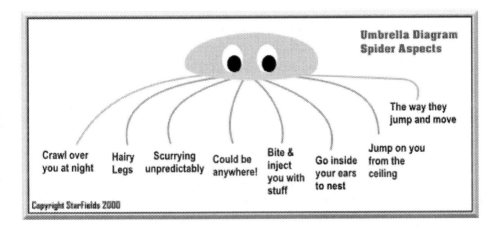

Originally designed by Chrissie Hardisty in 1999, the umbrella diagram is a simple but very useful representation. Take a blank piece of paper, write your issue at the top and make lines streaming out below towards the other aspects of the problem. For some clients, this is a very supportive and important device to "bring these aspects out into the open" as well as a useful guiding mechanism for the practitioner to both plan and then track a session that involves many aspects – you can soon enough forget one of the most important ones, especially if there is much high drama and interesting or appalling content to be dealt with, and/or the session stretches out in time over many appointments.

Also for the testing phase, the original Umbrella diagram can be both a really clear and positive convincer experience for therapist and client alike – yes, you have cleared all these things, there's nothing remaining, the intervention is tidy and it is **complete**.

Simultaneous Aspects

This is a particular interest in the treatment of trauma, i.e. a single, extremely highly charged experience that may have been very short in duration. What you will find with most memory based problems is that although the events may have taken a long time, there are brief instances of "flares" – pinpoint moments where the intensity of the situation and experience breached the ordinary thresholds and caused major change in someone's neurology.

These single "flares" of incidences can have numerous major aspects that all happened virtually at the same time; sometimes in the treatment of such "flares" it seems that you have treated everything but the charge is still most significant or hasn't changed significantly although the memory was treated repeatedly.

In these cases, you are often looking at an incident of Simultaneous Aspect formation.

Here is an example:

I saw a lady who had been involved in a traffic accident caused by a head on collision with a driver at night who was on the wrong side of a dual carriageway, i.e. going in the wrong direction altogether in the wrong lane at high speed.

She was suffering from severe PTSD symptoms and although the memory was treated numerous times, it still wasn't anywhere near released or even relieved.

The aspects were simultaneous at the moment just before impact – all at the same time in a split second.

- There was the light from the oncoming car, incredibly bright, blinding out everything.

- There was the screeching of the tyres.

- There was the screaming of the children in the back seat.

- There was the sound of her own voice screaming.

- There was the thought that she had now killed her children.

- There was the pain in her foot as she tried to drive the brake pedal through the floor of the car.

- There was the smell of the burning tyres.

Every one of them needed to be treated in its own right to have the memory take its rightful place and the main PTSD symptoms to dissolve.

Sequential Aspects

This particular lady had more residue from the accident than just the PTSD flashbacks. There were more aspects to do with many other things and these were unfolding sequentially in time before, during and after the accident and the court case that followed.

- There were experiences such as coming to briefly in the mangled wreck of her car and there being a silence of voices – the children weren't screaming anymore.

- There was a moment when she awoke briefly on the ambulance stretcher and saw a black rubber body bag on another stretcher nearby.

- There was terrible pain and trauma in the hospital – incident upon incident.

I would like to note that sequential aspects are best unravelled from the genesis point onward, i.e. to treat the oldest ones first as they may collapse the entire "string of pearls" and no further treatments may be necessary.

Testing EFT Treatments

If we return to the treatment flow for a moment, and in the context of aspects, of course each aspect of any given presenting problem is a mini treatment that follows the same flow from enquiring into the problem through to the successfully completed test.

The test is an absolutely crucial part of the treatment and I cannot impress upon you highly enough just how important it is in the scheme of things – indeed, I would say that without a test the treatment is entirely incomplete, wasteful, untidy and entirely undesirable in all ways.

The Purposes Of Testing

First of all, the purpose of testing is to actually know when you and your client are ready for a test and when the main and often initial treatment has been successfully completed.

Why is it important to know when that part of the treatment is over and we are moving into the next segment in the treatment flow?

It is important for the therapist/practitioner/operator to know where they are and to keep control of the procedure both in time and direction because you can easily talk sessions to death or get sidetracked into a whole new trauma or issue area at this point, which can leave a session feel incomplete and confused, as though nothing has really been done and nothing was properly explored or resolved. Clients will feel unhappy with such an outcome, as of course will the practitioner after they leave, wondering where it all went wrong.

In that context, knowing **when to move into the testing phase** sets both the time and the direction for the next steps that need to be taken, based on the feedback received from the client, for example:

- "No, I don't feel I am ready to (look at the rat, meet my mother, get into the lift, live without my addictive substance/behaviour, change my mind about X, etc), **because...**"

Clearly, we need to do some more work with aspects here – there is something very important still unresolved. This is might not come up **ever and at all** unless you bring up the subject of the test.

Agreeing On A Test

If you recall, we have already mentioned that before you start the treatment, at the enquiry stage, it would be a very good idea to discuss a test with the client that would have both of you in no doubt as to whether the problem has been resolved successfully or significant progress in the right direction achieved.

The standard phrasing for this is:

"How will you know when your issue has been resolved? What would you think, feel, do that is different and that will let us know that we have resolved your issue successfully?"

There is true merit in spending some time in devising a test that will serve as a **convincer** to the client – have the client really and completely know the treatment has worked and they are able to be and do differently than before.

The reason for this is that many times, things change during EFT treatments – but they change structurally, unconsciously and at a deep level. If the client is not **consciously aware** that these changes have taken place, they will **continue to act as though there was no change** at all; they will continue to do, think and be as before. If this seems a little abstract, consider a poor person who had a large sum deposited into their bank account but no-one told them. Of course, they would not think to check and of course, they would continue to behave as though they had no money because as far as they are concerned, it is still "the" reality.

For example, a lady with a severe height phobia was treated but the **convincer and test** was not executed by the practitioner at the time. For nearly a year she continued to **believe** that she was still afraid of heights and never tried to climb a ladder or go to the top floor of a building – until an accident forced this and to her total amazement she found that the fear wasn't there anymore – she had been afraid of something that had left but she hadn't know that!

It is never and absolutely not enough for **you** to know that the problem has been resolved – the client must know it too and must be **convinced** that this is so.

Especially with long standing problems that have involved so very many failed attempts and failed efforts in the past (especially with chronic problems and with addictions including weightloss) it is not that easy to convince a client that their problem has been resolved successfully and may require more than one test as well as having temporal components such as "Will it come back tomorrow?".

The Golden Rule Of Testing: Actions Speak Louder Than Words.

It is the client's new actions that will convince both them and you that the treatment is working or starting to work and that **something has changed**. Everything else – thoughts, feelings, what they say, what you say – may or may not be simply wishful thinking, illusion or hallucination.

Fear Of Testing

It is true that many practitioners – even very famous and experienced ones – will back away from the testing of the work that was done. They are often met half way by their clients who also don't want to test for their own reasons, and between them forge a silent conspiracy to omit that step in the treatment flow.

The reasons for this may well include:

- **Fear of Failure.**

If all looks pretty good on the surface and the client declares in moving tones how much better they feel and how convinced they are that the problem has gone completely, why risk "spoiling it all" by going outside and doing the real test and possibly **failing** it. There would be much automatic bad feelings of "oh dear" and general inadequacy on everyone's part and it is tempting to avoid having to have those.

- **Time Considerations.**

If the session was an hour scheduled and now we're at 55 minutes, of course a failed test would add on another half hour for looking for other aspects or lead to unfinished feelings and let-down – especially if the practitioner promised a "one session and all is well" approach in their advertising brochure.

Whatever the "resistance to testing" may be, please note that testing **will** really enhance your confidence in the techniques and make you understand how things work and what has to be done to **really make things work** with our forms of treatment in a way that nothing else could.

When we are working with EFT, our paradigm is always Failure=Feedback and whatever the outcome of the test, it will clearly prescribe the next step that needs to be taken as a totally helpful and supportive part of the entire process that is a meridian energy therapy treatment. In our case, it reads Failure=Feedback=Next Step and that is worth not only remembering profoundly, but also to explain to the clients if necessary – it makes the process far more controlled, far less scary and much more proactive and exciting.

* Please take another look at the treatment flow chart now and give attention to No 7, the test, and the three options presented there as to how to go on no matter what the actual outcome of the test may have been.

Designing Tests

Basically, you have a choice of just two approaches. One is a version of a physical test – being in the presence of the trigger in reality, in a real situation, with real people, circumstances, substances.

*****A SERIOUS SAFETY WARNING!!!*****

Severe phobias and responses of any kind – abreactions – must be tested with extreme caution. You could kill a client by exposing them to the trigger too early or too directly. The client can die of anaphylactic shock or have a stroke or a heart attack.

*****YOU HAVE BEEN WARNED.*****

The other option is to test mentally in some way, for example by using the MindWalk technique which basically involves imagining the situation. Within both the MindWalk and the physical tests there is a number of disassociation steps to make the testing procedure as gentle and effective as possible.

Disassociation In Discussion & Testing

It is important to be able to control the levels of distance between the client and their problem; **the distance being always directly proportional to the client's ability to still retain a sense of safety and control.**

With true trauma, there is no control and this is why each re-play of the traumatic incident in the form of a flashback, a panic attack, a violent allergic reaction and so forth serves to become a new trauma in its own right, each time it occurs.

Phobias – true phobias, not mild dislikes or beings somewhat scared of something – have this aspect of loss of control in common with PTSD type problems and are a good example as to the other forms of disassociation.

In general, we can put some distance between the client and problem in two ways, namely physical distancing and psychological distancing.

Physical Distancing

This would include

- objects and creatures (spiders, telephones, mice, needles, etc.)
- locations (lifts, motorways, airports, graveyards etc)
- substances (allergies, addictions)

For example, if someone was petrified of lifts, you could take them physically to a location where a lift exists and have them be at physical distances from the lift which will correspond exactly to their internal barometer of fear – 100 steps = Fear at 1, 50 steps = Fear at 5.

This is a very simple yet very helpful way of both handling the safety aspects as well as having immediate visible feedback for all concerned as to how the problem is receding after each treatment round and I recommend it highly. It may not look as elegant as just waving your hands but for many clients, this direct approach that really creates a new experience as well at the same time as releasing the old fears and limitations with the test right there is much, much appreciated and in many ways, represents the "ultimate convincer experience".

The second form of creating distance is by

Psychological Distancing

The first one of these approaches is using keywords and symbols for the experience rather than to talk about the experiences, memories or emotions directly. Here is a brief reminder of the most commonly used basic techniques.

MindWalk Techniques

All MindWalk techniques rely on creating an experience in the person's mind – sounds, pictures, feelings, sensations and the corresponding mind/body/energy totality states which derive from the experience.

As with all the other types of techniques, there are levels of association/disassociation.

How deeply a client associates into the experience, is entirely in your hands.

It is down to the instructions you are giving the client at the time as to how close or deep they will get to the actual memory; is a VERY IMPORTANT POINT for you to know and realise at all times.

Here are examples of the instructions you might give the client:

Full Association

- Remember clearly back to that day. What is the time of year, what are you wearing? What is the weather like? What are you seeing/hearing/feeling right here, right now?

You are directly asking the client to access the range of experiences stored – kinaesthetic memories that will draw the client to **be right back there** and totally associated.

Details make the memory more real, and the more detail, the more real the experience becomes. Also note the temporal language being used – when the client says, "I am standing outside my home with my teddy bear and I am terrified.", using first person, present tense, you know we are really there and talking full association.

This is absolutely the same as a hypnotic age regression. You might also notice that clients access this state by accident or as a matter of course in the course of a treatment and then you can decide as to whether you want to work here or if you want to get some distance for safety.

For severe problems and true trauma, you do everything you can to avoid the client getting into this full body memory associated state – I know you know by now but I thought I'd remind us all once again!

Cognitive Disassociation

As we noted, the language used directs the experience and gives us the key to where the client is and what is going on inside them. Past tense is a good disassociation marker and device:

"What **were** you wearing that night?" – "I was wearing a green sweater."

Talking **about** the experience or memory rather than re-telling it is also of this nature and it is this form of cognitive disassociation that is the usual way in which we deal with past memories quite naturally.

Directed Cognitive Disassociation

Here we use creative cognitive techniques to distance the client from the events in their memories. A good basic example is the NLP technique of having the client and therapist go to a cinema together in their mind's eye and play the movie of the events on the screen.

This allows for more levels of cognitive disassociation – the movie can be played in black and white, made fuzzy to start with or be quite small or the client might sit in the back row close to the exit; you can disassociate this even further by having the client be in the projectionist's booth high above, watching themselves watching the sequence of events.

There are many variations on this theme; one being to have an adult self watch the events from a 3rd party perspective and another, quite natural one is to have the story of events told in the form of "This didn't happen to me, but there was this friend of mine ...." which people often do to protect themselves automatically when the topic matter is too disturbing or embarrassing.

MindWalks are called thus because here, you are directing the client to a sequence of events, once again exactly like a hypnotic induction or guided meditation so you can find aspects and test situations, circumstances and events with the client physically being safe in the office.

For example, someone who has a phobia of air travel may be guided to a MindWalk that starts all the way back when they are packing their bags and thinking about the journey, to the night before, to the waking in the morning, getting ready, calling the taxi, what they are thinking whilst they are in the taxi, getting to the airport, getting out of the taxi and the doors opening to that special airport light and airport smell and so on.

MindWalks are exactly like the story protocol or real life tests – as soon as the client shows any kind of disturbance or fear, you stop and treat the issue that has arisen, or the aspect that has become revealed.

They also serve as a good secondary form of test before the event.

Remember once again the rules of mental association as you direct a MindWalk experience:

- The language of time and self you are using in instructing the client sets the depth and power of the experience – "You are standing on the hard marble floor with your suitcase heavy and your ticket in your hand" is first person to the client, present tense.

- The more detail, the more real the internal experience becomes. The less detail, the less real and more disassociated.

In the MindWalk, you can test for **worst case scenarios** and push the limits of what the client thought they could handle before the treatment began.

EFT Homework Protocols

The second to last step in the EFT treatment flow is the homework assignments, or what we suggest the client do with themselves and by themselves at home.

I had a very interesting experience with a client who had cancer. She was rightfully extremely scared and upset and felt that the simplicity of EFT was absolutely an insult to the severity of her problem.

This happens not just with cancer, but many clients have suffered so long and so much, they really do regard "just tap under the eye and see – you never needed to suffer at all, you fool!" as the ultimate insult to be heaped upon their many injuries already sustained.

With this particular cancer patient, I wanted to really make sure that she would get the benefits of the energy therapies to take with her into the unfolding events of operations, chemotherapy, radiotherapy and the nights in between when she was alone with her pain and fear – I did not want her to storm out of my office in disgust.

So I changed tack and proceeded, for the next two hours, to laboriously muscle test her to find a custom algorithm for each one of her main areas of fears, pains and discomforts and thoughts that would go round and round in her head.

Some of these had sequences of 40 or more tapping points which I wrote out, one by one, on many sheets of paper. Some were shorter and I deliberately manipulated the muscle testing so she would have short algorithms for moments of crisis, especially in the hospital after the treatments which left her totally devoid of energy and extremely weak.

The client left happily, much relieved, with all those sheets of algorithms.

She recovered very quickly from the operation and send me a Thank You card, saying that the algorithms had been her life savers.

This is a real story in point. EFT helps people. As far as I am concerned, I really don't care what YOU have to do to have people be comfortable with the protocols, and sometimes it needs a little song and dance or doing something that is neither strictly mechanically necessary nor what you would be doing by choice or preference to **get the job done**.

This is so with all problems people might bring to you, but most especially with the very serious health challenges that you need to **go with the client** and not against them.

Use their belief systems, whatever they may be, and move into that – EFT becomes completely mechanical when I talk to someone who is a systems engineer, and completely esoteric when I talk to a lady in a purple floor length skirt wearing a crystal on a silver chain and Celtic symbols on her many scarves.

There are many ways, many metaphors in which to describe the processes of "tapping on meridian points" and not one is righter or better than any other.

I am bringing this up in conjunction with the homework protocols especially because if the client walks out and basically chucks the card with the EFT points on your drive as they are striding away, a very, very bad thing has happened and an opportunity for healing has been horribly wasted – and not by the client, at that.

Do NOT imagine for one moment that all clients will do what you tell them once they have left the office. They need to have whatever you have decided between the two of you as the most helpful and beneficial course of action clear in their minds and they must **want to do it** – I have mentioned this before but now's the time to really say it again.

Next, your homework advice MUST fit in with the client's life style.

I discussed with my cancer client, for example, exactly what her visits to the hospital were like and how the treatments were progressing to find out just where and when she would be tap, where it would be right for her to do it, and even down to where she would keep the sheets with the algorithms so she could find them easily.

In order to decide on the right homework assignments explained in the right way to a client, it is of the essence that you should understand the life they are leading, and if the client happens to be yourself you really must open your eyes, let the illusions go and become aware of how and when you can fit a treatment session **seamlessly** into that person's existing life in such a way that it will be really easy to remember, really easy to do, and bring immediate benefits.

We will come back to these principles in the section on treating addictions because it is so important that the healing doesn't end when the session is over – the session with the therapist or the meditation session with yourself – but indeed, becomes a part of the person's life, an ongoing commitment to themselves and their health that pervades everything, not just a few stolen moments of time off in moments of desperation.

Homework assignments and the client's response to what is being proposed is rightfully, a treatment all by itself as objections become apparent, the therapist learns more about the realities of the life the client is leading, as "anti-healing" beliefs and ideas about not being able to help oneself at all come to the fore in the discussion of what tapping is to be conducted for what in between treatment sessions in the magic circle of the therapist's office – outside of space, time and any reality.

This is why I have homework as such an important part of the treatment flow – when this is treated with the true attention it deserves, and moves from simply handing over a card with the tapping points at the end of the session with a vague, "Yeah you can just tap a bit when you need to ..." to a real and true prescription for health in the most holistic and ecological sense possible.

"Supervision"

This is not a special power that allows you to see through walls and other solid objects, but the idea that the client can call you and ask for further help outside of the "magic circle" of the paid for treatment session.

Many therapists offer said supervision in the form of what I call "the Suzi question", named after the niece of an elderly client of mine who would phone once every three months and in a weak voice ask, "Is there anything you want me to do?"

The elderly lady in question needed all the help in the universe – from shopping, to house cleaning, to being accompanied to the doctor's, having her medication picked up, to simply a bit of moral support, attention, someone to come in unexpectedly and just have a cup of tea with her – well, you get the picture.

But Suzi never did anything other than say these words in such a way that my client always sighed and answered, "No, thanks for offering ..."

I guess much like our friend Suzi, one might get scared and overwhelmed of getting sucked too deeply into caretaking for another and thus, best not to start at all! However, it is possible to design **integral support structures** for clients that will give them a feeling of safety and being able to safely ask for further help and which, if rightfully employed in all ways (and this includes being paid for appropriately) would make the whole joined healing endeavour so much more powerful than otherwise possible.

I have included these considerations for the many excellent healers, coaches and counsellors who have not had rigorous psychotherapy style training on how to create workable contracts of supervision with clients, so that they might give some thought to this very important structural part of the treatment flow (and indeed, the client flow!).

Here are the main points of the Homework Protocol once more in brief:

1. Make sure the client understands the homework.

2. Deal with any objections the client might have about doing the homework.

3. Future pace to test for any objections (hypnotherapists can use this to install desired outcome states and pre-memories) and pre-familiarise the client with the homework procedures/protocols.

4. Adjust homework protocol to fit right in with client's life style and way of thinking and doing.

5. Give relevant handouts.

6. Discuss supervision.

Overall Energy Re-Balancing

Now here is an interesting piece of research I conducted in late 1999 in response to a hunch I had about the apex effect and a number of related topics, including the referral frequency of people who had very successfully overcome various traumas, problems and phobias with EFT.

Simply put, the referral rates were abysmal.

It would have stood to reason to expect that someone who had overcome a life long phobia in a single session or had an epiphany breakthrough on a personal issue would tell all their friends and family about how great EFT was and the therapist/counsellor who administered it – but this was not the case. In fact, referrals from existing clients across the board was markedly less for many EFT practitioners than one would expect for the average dentist or hypnotherapist.

However, in the group of EFT therapists there was one section for which the opposite held true – the Reiki practitioners who **also gave the clients a general Reiki-balancing** at the end of the session and before they sent them home got more re-bookings, kept their clients for longer and got referrals from existing clients **above** the expected rate for the healing professions.

In hindsight, this is actually completely obvious and clearly logical.

EFT treatments shake up the energy system rather dramatically and often, clients are very much in a daze as something has happened they have no previous experience of and no previous frame of reference for. It is simply easier to explain the whole thing away or just to forget about it than to consciously begin to undo all the beliefs, structures, thoughts etc about well being and open up this whole new world which includes meridians, energy systems and the possibility of a trauma "just disappearing" but for a few taps on your face, body and hands.

An overall re-balancing and stabilising of the energy systems before the client leaves the office will go a very long way to counterbalance the effects of this and at the very least, will leave the client **feeling good** – bright, alive, positive.

Even if that is all they remember about the treatment, the session and the therapist, of course it is already enough that when talk comes around amongst friends or at work of someone needing help with something, that they are much more likely to remember their EFT treatments in a positive and beneficial light.

As there is no direct EFT "overall re-balancing protocol" to conduct at the end of the session, here are some energy based ideas to do instead:

Overall Energy Re-Balancing Techniques

1. If using EFT is of the essence, the "Channel Clearer" with a few well chosen suggestions along the way of "relaxing, releasing, feeling the flow and beginning to sparkle as the energies run clearly and smoothly through your body" is a very good option.

2. Standard overall re-alignment techniques from Reiki, therapeutic touch, touch healing, quantum touch and so forth; conducted with or without touch.

3. A mini-hypnosis session, quite conversationally done, which can be disguised as a blessing, a final relaxation session, or spoken straight with the client being aware and in co-operation with the energy re-balancing. Deep knowledge of hypnosis is not required as long as the main points are observed of keeping internal representations phrased in the positive and suggestions of general re-alignment and free and peaceful flow are spoken gently and with conviction.

4. The EmoTrance technique of "invoking innocent energy" in the form of an imaginary shower of pure, light, gentle energy which washes away all the residue from the treatment and leaves the client bright, sparkly and fresh in all ways.

5. If all or any of this is completely out of the question with this particular client and/or because of the working circumstances, the therapist may just request a moment of silence and relaxation and perform the overall alignment quietly, in proxy format, prayer for the client, performing the Reiki-style alignments with their "hands of ghost", imagining clearing light or the innocent energies and do the work in this way.

Energy Re-Balancing Conclusion

To sum up – of course, any client should leave feeling energised and better than when they arrived.

That goes without saying.

Life being as it is and people being as uniquely unique as they are, we cannot always achieve this. The overall energy re-balancing as the very last act before the client gets up to go completes any energy treatment session most successfully, either way and is a real gift to the client and also, to the therapist who too will leave the session with a sense of peace at least.

PART 2 – THE ADVANCED PATTERNS OF EFT

Energetic Relationships

Our story starts in the spring of 2000, in my then office which was a sitting room with sofas and paintings on the wall and a red carpet from Iran.

I was beginning to re-interpret the entire process of therapeutic relationships and changes in the human mind from the viewpoint of an energetic level, and a great many things that had been a mystery to me were becoming apparent and obvious at this time.

And then, the day came when I met Patsy.

An Introduction To The Concepts Of Energetic Relationships

I have a client on the couch.

She is an extremely talented healer, about fifty years old, and her problem is arthritis in her hands. Her knuckles are badly swollen as are all the joints, she can hardly move her wrists and she is in so much pain at times that she wants to cut off her hands to alleviate the suffering.

She has had any form of treatment under the sun for this condition she has been suffering from since she was a child - counselling, steroid injections, medication, healing, psychology, energy therapies, and nothing, but nothing has made any impact on the problem.

I've seen her before and got some relief and shifting but it is always temporary and the changes never stay and whilst she is talking about the week she's had, I'm de-focussed and just drifting in my mind.

She is telling me about how her arthritis has been playing up and it strikes me all of a sudden that she is referring to "her arthritis" in much the same way as my animal behaviour counselling clients used to refer to their animals:

"My arthritis really didn't like it when I tried to go out to clean the stables"

"I ate some cheese but my arthritis puts a stop to that"

"It always lets me know when I've overdone it".

Whilst she is saying this, she is making small movements with her hands across her lap (she cannot rest her hands on her legs because that is too painful, so they are hovering about half a foot in midair, rigid from the wrist, at all times) and it occurs to me it looks as though she is stroking **an invisible something** that has taken up residence there.

So I interrupt her in mid sentence and say, "If your arthritis had a name, what would it be?"

Surprised, she says, "Patsy?"

"And what colour is Patsy?"

"Patsy is pink!" the client says, surprised and laughing.

"And what is Patsy?"

"Well she's a cat, of course!" says the client and both of us start falling about at the notion of "Patsy, the pink arthritis cat".

That was really the first time that I began to look in consciousness as a problem as an energetic reality - Patsy was absolutely real, existing in the room with us, invisible bar the physiological manifestations in Mary's hands and Mary had an intense relationship with this energetic entity.

She was even sitting stroking it just like you would a cat on your lap!

Right from the start, it was blatantly clear to both Mary and I that we were not talking about a thought construct, a metaphor or an idea at all.

Not something that was "all in her mind" at all.

Patsy was real, and she was here. I could feel her, touch her, even see her in the shape of a small darkness or density that resided around Mary's hands. Now I am aware that I could have hallucinated this, and I probably did, but to all intents and purposes, how much realer can you get?

Mary had been living with this entity for the better part of 40 years. Even if it was "all in her mind" which I am convinced it was not (although I have no measurement or scientifically allowable evidence procedure to know beyond my own impressions and therefore cannot prove it to you), it was still real to her and therefore the whole point becomes moot altogether.

And now, and what with me having been an expert in the behavioural, psychological and physiological effects of relationships between animals and owners, a whole world of intriguing possibilities arose immediately.

One thing I needed to know right away was how much love there was between Mary and Patsy, for I have never known an owner to keep any pet animal when there wasn't.

People would have the most excruciating ongoing problems with their pets but if there was an underlying bond of love, they would put up with it literally forever. If there was not, they wouldn't even be here, seeking help, because they would have found a way to get rid of the problem (pet) in some shape or form.

Only if the pain exceeded the love, could this be done.

Looking at "love" as an energetic reality of a strand that connects someone to someone or something, by the way, is a useful exercise and shift in perception. Pain, similarly, is another kind of strand of a different flavour - you could think of one as nourishing and the other as destructive or depleting, if you wanted to.

But back to Mary. Her eyes nearly fell out when I asked about any possible love between her and her problem, and then she shook her head in real wonderment as she told me about how no matter what had gone on in her life, her arthritis had always been there; it had never left her nor ever failed to point out to her when she was overdoing certain things, or eating things she should not, and that, in fact, if it was to go, she "would simply not know what to do with herself or who or what she would be or become".

Now let's be very clear and precise here for a moment.

If you have read other of my publications, I have always had a problem with the concept of so called "Secondary Gain". Of course, problems have secondary gains, but what a lot of the therapist's community really and profoundly misunderstand is that it's not secondary at all most of the time, but the **Primary Reason** for having the problem in the first place. There is a genesis reason, the Primary Reason, for acquiring and keeping a problem, and apart from that, there are then many other positive benefits as of course, a person will take their lemon and make their lemonade; but it is extremely important to make the distinction between the Primary Gain and any possible secondary gains because if you don't, you can't really address the resistance to giving up the problem.

With Mary here however, we're not even talking about Primary Gain anymore at all. We're talking about positive emotions of tremendous depth and reach and range that have nothing to do with gains or relieving of pains but are born out of our neurology's inbuilt desire to make connections wherever we can and to give and receive positive energies such as love, affection, approval, attention and acceptance (you'll get to hear those 4 A's again!).

Although I saw Mary's connection with Patsy clearly and I already knew there would be positive regard from her to her problem, I had really no idea until that day of the strength and power of her emotions on the subject.

I think this day was too the day I finally understood how emotions are, indeed, the currency of our entire neurology. They are absolutely what drives us, and without the will and ability to understand emotions, really understand the power and intensity of how they affect us, there is no way on God's green earth to understand people at all, nor to even try and heal them.

Emotions and a true understanding of their power and their nature are what is and has been so sadly missing from the psychology paradigm. There is lip service given to them, yet the entire academic field is designed to be "third party" - detached from emotions and supposedly Spock-logical.

Little wonder that such a mind set cannot bring forth the required insights and changes! It's like someone trying to describe and map the nature of light but without ever looking at it directly - no wonder so much was missed before.

Even the more "enlightened" and "spiritual" approaches completely fail, in my opinion, to really deal with emotions - well how can you understand the subject if the only emotions you're allowed to have are some kind of nice, friendly feeling of relaxation, and all else is (tut tut!) undesirable and must be meditated away immediately?

Well, Mary went home this day deep in thought and extremely excited. She knew about the meridian energy therapies and did a lot of tapping around the subject of Patsy and her love-hate relationship with Patsy, from her own stand point, by proxy for Patsy and also for their relationship problems together and I am happy to say that it seems to have resolved the problem for her at last.

Lessons In Energy

Patsy was an absolute revelation to me about the nature of emotional entanglements with everything, and not just with a problem.

The very first thing that came to mind after Mary had left was my own emotional entanglements with a piece of blue cheese.

On my way to the fridge, I became aware that I was happy and excited and couldn't wait to see my friend who, in turn, was waiting for me inside, ready and willing to make me happy.

I opened the door, and searched around as you would at a railway station for a familiar face. Found my friend and extracted him with a big smile of anticipation and welcome recognition on my face. Brought him out and sat him on my hand and looked at him most lovingly.

Then I stopped, backed up and considered that I was having a most patsy-like relationship with that piece of blue cheese.

I put it on the work top in front of me, put my elbows down, rested my head on them and looked at my special friend and enemy in real consciousness for the first time in my life.

For the first time in my life, I consciously tracked my conflicting emotions about this energetic reality that sat there in front of me.

Here are some of the thoughts and feelings.

- Definitely gratitude. This entity makes me feel good. It replenishes me when I need to be replenished in a most specific way.

- Sensuous delight. This entity makes me physically feel good with its texture and its taste and structure. It does so without fail, every time I call on it, which brings me to this:

- Like Mary, there was absolutely a feeling of great gratitude and loyalty there. This thing never lets me down. It never says no to me or that I can't have what I want or need from it. It doesn't hold out on me, it doesn't make me jump through hoops and prove my worth and it available just for the asking. To experience these really strong feelings of gratitude was an amazing sensation for which I was quite unprepared.

But then, there was the conflict.

After all, I told myself every single time I took a bite that I should feel bad about it, that "every bite would go straight to my thighs", that I was stupid and weak for wanting to eat something that would make me even fatter, that I was "sinning" and "indulging myself" and that I should be ashamed of myself for even thinking of seeking this miserable support in this pathetic way.

Meeting my old friend, Mr Blue Cheese in this way, was an extraordinary experience. I would now most strongly invite you to take any kind of food whatsoever, and it doesn't have to be an old friend at all, and just track what comes into your mind when you allow it to come - fond memories, negative memories, thoughts, feelings and most of all, emotions tied to it.

You might also like to try and track the "affirmations" or "post hypnotic suggestions" you give yourself every single time you get in contact with this item.

The totality of those represents your energetic relationships with the thing, sets how good it is for you; most likely tells your auto-immune system exactly how to respond to it (that's a very important point!); and generally decides how stressed out you get in partaking of it.

You could write a whole book in and of itself about the ins and outs of this.

In the days that followed, we applied the pattern of energetic relationships to some of the following:

- ideas
- concepts
- landscapes
- people
- food

- money
- items of obsession
- clothing
- and just about everything else in the entire world!

All of these relationships, by the way, can of course be dis-entangled and eased and smoothed and brought back to a reasonably even flow first by the application of any energy therapy of your choice and in this case, by the application of EFT. You can read more about these energetic relationship patterns in the following sections now or later on.

In the meantime, once we had met Patsy, we began to understand that we were surrounded by ghosts.

Leverage & Targeting Interventions

In general, all energy therapies treatments are either target at:

1. At the presenting symptoms

or

2. At the causative event or core issues.

However, there is a third option which opens the way for very powerful changework indeed, and that is when we target our intervention in this particular instance:

3. At the energetic relationship level.

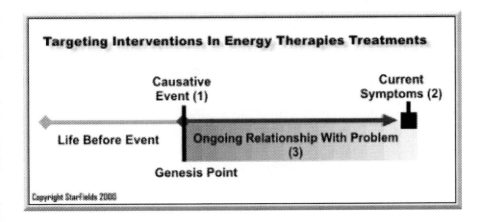

113

What is often overlooked is the fact that in the event was the birth or **genesis** of this whole new set of occurrences – you could call it a problem if you will; either way, from the event to the now, we have an ongoing relationship with the individual over time with the problem in their life.

The Process Of Forming An Energetic Relationship

Here are the steps of forming an Energetic Relationship in brief:

1. Awareness

2. Attention

3. Response - Emotion

4. Emotion Of Emotion

5. Conscious Thought

Let us now consider these in more detail.

Awareness

In order to have any kind of relationship with anything at all, you need to be aware of its existence, either consciously or unconsciously. The relationship really starts to become an Energetic Relationship, however, the moment you place your conscious awareness and your attention on that part of creation. Think of a hundred people in a bar. They are just people until one of them catches your eye for some reason - a beginning relationship is born in that moment.

How deep this relationship becomes and how meaningful to an individual is entirely dependent **on the strength of emotion** that is present in the context of that which you are having the relationship with.

In energetic terms, and as emotions are feedback devices to the state of the energy body, you could say that the depth of an energetic relationship with anything depends on how much impact it had on the energy system at the moment of first contact.

This can happen directly with people, ideas, objects and states of being or it can happen that by accident, already existing and resident emotions get tied to something that just happened to be there. (*See also "Guiding Stars" for more on this process*).

This is often the case with landscapes and homes, for example; in and of themselves they are not causing or creating the emotions but because they were present when the emotion was experienced, they get entangled in that particular relationship web.

Now, the occurrence has drawn our conscious attention and we **pay attention to it**, thereby feeding it and making it stronger as an occurrence. This is a basic law of energy and simply as it is – you have a pain, it takes your attention away from almost everything and quite the same if you fall in love; either way, this is now the next deepener to the emergent relationship network.

As the occurrence has had such a profound impact on the energy body, we experience strong and sometimes, entirely overwhelming emotions. As people are so unaware of the whys and wherefores of energetic realities and the principles of those systems, they are also generally unprepared for these emotions, especially if they are other or stronger than they have experienced before.

Point 5, i.e. Emotion of Emotion, is a secondary process that causes further entanglements. If you like something that you shouldn't like, you might feel bad about liking it, which is a secondary emotion tied to the same object of attraction.

Point 6, Conscious Thought, refers to making deliberate Free Will choices about certain things and engaging in activities designed to strengthen positive entanglements, deliberately. We also now have all kinds of counter-pulling sensations and emotions and attempts to rationalise these somehow, find some sort of reasons for the state of affairs, find solutions, and all of that without understanding any of what has been happening at the invisible layers of the energy system.

If we look at it like that, we can clearly understand why people get obsessed with their own problems – which continue to grow as more and more attention and energy is going their way, growing into these energetic entities over time that really seem to take on a life of their own.

Evolution Over Time

These kinds of "energetic entities" become denser and denser and in exact relationship to the impact they are having on a person's energy systems.

Here is a progression that shows what must have happened to cause the formation of these dense, self-sustaining energy systems.

- One time incident with no emotional charge – this tells us that the incident didn't change or affect the energy body.

- One time incident with residual emotional charge – this tells us that the energy body was changed a little.

- One time incident with high emotional charge – this incident had a serious impact on the energy body and changed it significantly.

- Multiple incidents with little or no emotional charge – you think of those as small energy occurrences that are expected to happen and will heal over time as the natural immune systems of the energy body seek to restore the original conditions.

- Multiple incidents with high emotional charge – here, the energy body gets warped more and more out of alignment and cannot recover its equilibrium naturally any longer. Every new occurrence adds to the misalignment.

- Ongoing incidents with ever strengthening bonds.

As you can see, the longer someone lives with an energetic reality, the more ways there are and the more opportunities for entanglements of one kind or the other.

The really interesting point is the last one, which is rarely found in human relationships but in relationships with things that make you feel good every time, such as chocolate, a dog that wags its tail when you come home, or all kinds of addictions and problems with massive Primary and Secondary gains.

The more and the more often something happens, obviously, the stronger the bonds become.

For Better Or For Worse

Names For Positive Energetic Bonds

- Gratitude,
- Fondness,
- Love,
- Attention,
- Safety,
- Peace,
- Harmony,
- Relief,
- Support,
- Belonging etc.

Negative:

- Fear,
- Pain,
- Anger,
- Grief,
- Bereavement,
- Shame,
- Guilt,
- Rage,
- Hatred,
- Panic,
- Out of Control,
- Physical Pain,
- Depression,
- Hopelessness etc.

The above are only a few labels for you to get started with.

Do bear in mind that people label their internal experiences of emotions in highly idiosyncratic ways, and one man's bereavement is never the same as that of another. When someone says, "depression" to you, know it is an approximation of an energetic, multidimensional state that is complex and always, always, absolutely personal to that one individual.

Deepening The Bonds

Energetic Relationship Bonds are deepened by:

- o **Time AND/OR**
- o **Intensity of Emotional Charge AND/OR**
- o **Presence AND/OR**
- o **Attention/Intention**

Especially when Intensity of Emotional Charge and Attention form a feedback loop, energetic relationship bonds become particularly dense and the more time passes, the more dense they become until they are hard and crystalline.

Internalising The Problem

A particular set of problems with energetic relationships emerges when the relationship becomes too personal, too close. This happens when the energy systems are set up now so that they will make the original disturbance a part of themselves. When this happens, the problem becomes "a part of me" – and then it has the same survival protection extended to it as has the original energy body and will resist resolution or removal in exactly the same way as a **healthy sub-system** is protected by the totality.

The problem system/disturbance is to all uses, practicalities and intents **inside** a person's wider energy body, or one could say that the **energy body extends itself** to **embrace** the problem with which these strong energetic bonds have been created.

It is then that a person will confuse the problem with the self – naturally – and will think of themselves as being "incomplete" without the problem.

This systemic is also sometimes referred to in terms of "identity reversals".

The Core Concepts Of Energetic Relationship Work

Practical Problems With Real Life Relationships

Interestingly enough, energetic relationships really and profoundly mirror real life relationships an individual has with real other people and real objects of one kind or the other.

It is therefore reasonable to presume that there is an underlying set of strategies at work for "relationships" in general which covers all of an individual's relationships, in the hard or energetically based. This has the interesting effect that energetic relationships work on an addiction can lead to transformational insights and changes to personal relationships with human beings.

A Problem As An Energetic Entity

To look at any problem as an Energetic Entity over time allows for a multi-dimensional approach to it. It allows for integration of conflicting emotions, thoughts and approaches; it de-mystifies and de-demonifies the problem in the process and gives it a shape and form so we can deal with it in consciousness. This is very important indeed and very empowering, too.

Conceptualising Our Problems

It is very difficult indeed to be talking at all about such a thing as, say, a "heroin addiction". What IS that? You can't put it in a wheelbarrow, you can't DO anything with it at all.

When I say "conceptualising" a problem I do NOT necessarily mean "visualising", although there's an aspect of that if you would want to make use of it. Visualising a problem (Mary's Patsy became "a cat shape") is of course very useful but not necessarily the only approach. You can conceptualise a problem by bringing it down to the actual behaviours it entails, as an energetic entanglement, or even as a set of bar charts of conflicting emotions.

Organic VS Mechanical Approaches

The underlying metaphors employed in any form of conceptualisation (which is what we do all the time in order to translate our experience of reality and all its patterns into something we can manipulate in consciousness) are of prime importance for they set the limits of what can and cannot be achieved in any given field of endeavour (note the metaphor of field. That's a flat thing. Hence I use StarFields which is firstly at least three dimensional, but as there's more than one overlaying one another, we're talking multi-dimensional right from the concept's basic metaphor. As stars are of course, natural and organic rather than mechanical or man made, we retain the depth and developmental possibilities inherent in the metaphor as well).

When you are conceptualising with yourself or a client, and you give a problem a name or a shape, I would urge you to go for an organic metaphor as opposed to a mechanical one. For example, the heart is often likened to a clock. That's a strictly mechanical metaphor and you can see, hear and feel right away how incredibly limited that is - a clock cannot rebuild itself, it cannot grow, it cannot change, it cannot speed up and slow down in response to its environment, and so on and so forth.

Patsy being a cat, for example, has so much more richness, volition, ability and capability for having a relationship with, that it is actually a wonderful example of this process in action.

The Richness Of Relationship Bonds & Patterns

Never - NEVER! - underestimate the richness of relationship patterns and bonds.

Realise also that in any relationship system, you are dealing with a SYSTEM and the single person you are seeing in front of you is not a detached, unique thing that exists all by itself. You cannot do therapy with a fish removed from water (well not for long!) and you MUST consider the client as a part of their entire systems, which comprise their real families as well as their energetic families!

Family Therapy For Energetic Relationships:

The Harmony Programme Principles

1. Acknowledge The Reality

That means nothing more and nothing less than that you look at things as they really are and say, ok, so this is where we are. No judgement, no nothing. Just a straightforward acknowledgement. "Ok so you are spending £150 a day on crack. That's the truth and look at that, the sky hasn't fallen!"

2. Respect The Reality

There is NOTHING to be gained by ever tutting, freaking out, looking down on or generally speaking being ANYTHING OTHER than TOTALLY respectful of the client and their own SUBJECTIVE experiences. From this follows as night must follow day that you MUST:

3. Respect The Reality Of Emotion

If someone tells you they're in love with their venereal disease, so be it. That is THEIR experience. Do not EVER presume to tell them they are wrong to feel the way they do or even imply it by body posture, presupposition or even haste in "trying to change them into better people".

This is of course true for any kind of therapy, but when you're working with the intense emotions people have to their own worst demons, it is absolutely essential that you should remain completely respectful at all times - because if you don't, the demons won't come to the bargaining table at all!

4. Understanding Energy Exchanges In Relationships

If emotion is the currency of the mind, then attention is the currency of relationships. Attention is what transfers energy from one part of the system to the other, and in general, the parts of the system (the person and the energetic entity that is their problem/s) are somewhat starved of the required amounts of this energy at the frequency levels of affection, attention, approval and acceptance - or love, for short.

Many people and their systems have learned the hard way that the only way they can get attention at all is to seek negative attention - play up, be naughty, offend, scream loud enough, cause injury and pain, and you're sure to be noticed.

As the negotiator in an energetic relationship, it is your job to make sure that positive frequency attention is provided to both parties and that they learn to use those instead of the other kind.

5. Outcome Orientation

Through all you do, and however you do it, keep a clear outcome orientation in mind. What is it that the parts of the system want and need from each other? How can this be achieved? What is the end outcome for both parties? Once you know this (and take another look at the first 3 items again, for if you don't honour those, you will NEVER get to find out!) you can plot your course to get you there.

6. Feedback Devices

How do you know your interventions are working and you are on the right track? You need to agree feedback devices and mechanisms with your client and with your client's energetic realities.

In Mary's case, the pain from her arthritis was the perfect feedback device; when this diminished to the point of not being a reliable mechanism anymore, we turned to the visible swellings on her knuckles and the range of flexibility in her wrists was the last remaining feedback device.

7. Long Term Structural Maintenance

When you have dealt with the reasons for Patsy's existence, have successfully healed her and re-integrated her into Mary's energetic matrix in a most ecological and respectful way, we have to take a look at the long term structural maintenance, which brings up questions such as how Mary is going to get the benefits Patsy was providing in her absence (because if you don't deal with that, the problem or a problem like it MUST come back somehow) and what other changes are necessary to have a completely and fully stable end outcome that is self generative and will remain so until the end of Mary's days.

Energetic Relationships In EFT Treatments

Understanding Emotional Components

When we're talking Patsy type relationships, it is very clear that the emotional components are not restricted to the significant emotional experiences that caused Patsy to come into being.

Of course, in any event, you might want to begin your interventions at the genesis point, because you might not need to go any further. In a great many cases, clearing the genesis point is enough. In some others, it is not and the problem either doesn't recede enough (as had been the case with Mary) or it keeps coming back (which indicates strands having been left intact that keep feeding the energetic entity that is the problem and re-growing and re-vitalising it over time).

You will be looking at a whole array of relationship related emotions when you are working within this paradigm, right down to "bereavement" for both the problem when it has gone, as well as for "the person I used to be" (read the twin star system the person used to be).

I am not going to draw up long lists of emotions for you to tick off. It isn't necessary and it doesn't help you to develop your therapeutic abilities. Look carefully at your client and ASK THEM instead exactly how they are feeling about it all.

They will tell you in their own words and with precision as they are the ultimate experts on their problems and what it is **really** like to live with these, day in, day out.

Targeting The Interventions Correctly

One of the delightful things about the energetic relationships style of working is that everyone gets to have their say, and everyone gets to have their emotions released and healed and soothed. Remember our old EFT adage No 1 - **The Truth Shall Set You Free.**

It is quite extraordinary how deeply clients appreciate being able to speak freely about their feelings and not to have to be ashamed of them, or have to think themselves insane for having them in the first place. Emotional charge removal treatments should be targeted from the person's viewpoint, the problem's viewpoint, and from the overall viewpoint of what the highest outcome is for the client.

Opening Statements & Set Up Phrases

If you have conceptualised the problem or named it, use this for the keyword in the interventions. If this was not appropriate, name the problem - in these examples, instead of Patsy that would read "my (or the) arthritis". Consult with your client and go with their preferences in the matter absolutely.

Example Set Ups:

- I hate Patsy.
- She has ruined my life.
- She has saved me from myself.
- I am so grateful to Patsy.
- She has caused me so much pain.
- I would miss her so much if she was gone.
- I can't imagine my life without her.
- I don't want her to be a part of me.

Of course, in true relationship counselling we need to take the other party's point of view into consideration. In EFT treatments, this is achieved by using proxy set ups to shift perspective to the other partner.

Proxy set ups:

- Patsy is limiting me.
- Patsy doesn't understand me.

"I, Patsy" variations:

- I am Patsy. I must control Mary.
- I must stop her from ...
- I must protect her from ...
- I love her although she ...
- I serve her by ....

Blocks, Resources, Ecology

As the problem at one time was a fully integrated part of the person in question, it always, always contains resources that Patsy has now but Mary doesn't have anymore. One of the main attractions in most cases is to bring these resources home. In some cases (as we will see in the next section) there may be a fear of these resources or they may be perceived as possibly damaging, dangerous or even evil.

This will have to be addressed and healed - we're talking limiting beliefs and misunderstandings here which clean up beautifully and in consciousness when EFT is applied to them.

Take your time to discuss ecology with your client and take care to address all issues that arise in that context or else your intervention will not hold. As above, usually these are just limiting beliefs and new solutions can be found easily once the fear of such things as change and growth have been removed.

Example Set Ups:

- Patsy can control me when I cannot control myself;
- Patsy protects me when I fail to protect myself.

Long Term Ecology & Maintenance

If you have concluded a most thorough intervention - or so you thought! - but the problem reoccurs nonetheless, don't panic! You and your client have overlooked an important reason for keeping the problem. Remember the TOTE model and go back to the beginning.

What can and does happen after an EFT treatment session or range of sessions is that you have created a shift in the client's neurology which reveals, like an earthquake, old ruins that were previously buried and completely invisible.

People's minds are very complex and some types of long standing problems have a great many cross-contextual links across a great many gestalts and topic areas.

From things like simple phobia cures and allergies, we are used to working real fast with EFT - one session, all is well. Some things, such as Mary and her long standing relationship with Patsy, have strands that touches virtually every part of someone's life and they need a little bit more time and dedication, to work with the patterns of mind as they unfold to you and your client, and more than a single session is not only required, it is essential to create transformational shifts in safety.

Energetic Relationships Healing Step By Step

1. **Honest Assessment**

2. **Conceptualisation Stage**

3. **Respect**

4. **Needs, Wants, and Outcomes**

5. **Re-Structuring The Relationship**

6. **Ecology & Harmony**

7. **Resources**

8. **Long Term Feedback**

Honest Assessment (Client "Resistance")

I don't want to unbalance this system; I am afraid to challenge this; I don't want to look at this; I don't want to/ I am afraid to change (because ...?); I honestly believe that this problem is actually a part of me.

Conceptualisation Stage

This, my problem, is like ...

Respect

Deals with fear, resentment, and limiting beliefs about self and other: I cannot overcome this, cannot live without it, cannot win against it; and sets the path for communication and acceptance.

Needs, Wants, and Outcomes

Establishes both (all) parties needs, wants and outcomes prior to re-negotiating the entire relationship according to Harmony rules.

Re-Structuring The Relationship

This is the central point where the real work takes place according to what has been discovered and agreed upon.

Ecology & Harmony

Checks ecology and tests following the interventions above; Harmony is the highest organising principle not symptom cessation.

Resources

Remaining aspects, limiting beliefs, practical considerations, homework.

Long Term Feedback

Guiding Stars & EFT

Introduction

I have long been looking for a way to create transformational shifts with Meridian Energy Therapies; for I well knew they had the power to accomplish this if only they were leveraged in the right way.

I have been applying these therapies long term, for years now, daily to my own personal problems and I am in constant contact with a group of highly intelligent, dedicated people who have been doing exactly the same. What you will read here is not a supposition or a proposal.

This is the experience and my breakthrough on the nature of how our personalities are held together, and how we can re-structure them now if we wish to do so. In the process, you will have to be aware that you will unleash emotions of a range of power that you might not have experienced before.

For some applications, it will be impossible to work by yourself and you will need a support network beyond that currently found in 50 minute therapy hours. I hope you will find a friend or a therapist who can understand this and will be available to you when you require them.

Models Of Personal Development

It didn't actually occur to me at all until after the fact that we have a most peculiar model for various mind-body disturbances of the neurosomatic form and mental illness, and more importantly, that we have falsely been trying to apply these peculiar models when it comes to transformational and beneficial changes that are generalised and sweeping.

Consider this.

People do indeed, mostly lead lives of quiet or not so quiet desperation. I appreciate that this is a vast and high chunk observation, but the fact of the matter is that true, long lasting happiness, sexual ecstasy, deep and profound fulfilment in work or play and heart stopping moments of connection with our loved ones are either entirely out of our reach, or so rare and unusual that people build statues to them.

What do we have instead?

Well, there's the great majority of people who go on with their various miseries as best they can, swallow their headache tablets on a regular basis and contain themselves to moaning to friends over coffee or in the pub, stuck in jobs they don't like and relationships that are not what they hoped they would be, waiting for their two week holidays a year and the weekends "to start living", wearing themselves to grey and nothingness by the time they are 75.

Then there's the next category, those who are quite aware there's something wrong but continue to medicate themselves best they can with various forms of addictions, eating too much, burying themselves in work to take their minds of it, and so forth.

Then there's the ones who cannot ignore all that's unhappy, depressing, panic attack causing and those who treat them - the clients and the therapists, and I include in that category those who one might call personal developers and who get their therapy in a second hand form from books, workshops and audio tapes instead.

The patterns in this book were specifically developed for this last group to which I belong, as do most of my friends and colleagues. We found Meridian Therapies and most notably, EFT, and pounced upon it, heart and soul.

We tapped and tapped and tapped and discussed and thought and investigated as to how we could have better lives. And in truth, we managed to make some minor changes that greatly improved our ability to keep on functioning - such as being able to drive your car again, being able to get on an airplane, having no more fear of public speaking and so forth. Yet, for many, the long term practical repercussions were actually not what they had hoped for as structurally, and in real, practical, down to Earth terms, very little seemed to have changed in our lives.

We were still having fundamental problems with relationships, no matter how much we tapped; many of us were still having fundamental problems with self esteem, self image, self concept; many more were still having abundance related problems and after 2-3 years - YEARS! - of tapping one memory after another, one issue after another, that really wasn't good enough anymore.

Let me make something quite clear. At the time when we first started, the results we got were absolutely miraculous and helped us NO END.

Not for a single moment do I wish to take away from the power of EFT in the way it was then applied for problem solving, indeed I am absolutely convinced that without the pre-work I have done, I would not have been able to discover what I did, do the research nor write this section at all.

I am now talking about long term and deep level, transformational change.

- Such as a transformation from someone who was blatantly unsuccessful, to being shiningly successful (be this with women, in relationships, in health, as a parent, as a therapist, in business etc).

- Such as from someone who hates themselves to being congruent and at peace.

- Such as from someone who continually self sabotages and abuses themselves to being effective, balanced and powerful.

- Such as from experiencing life as a never ending treadmill with a few highlights here and there, to someone who flows with life and whose days are a never ending festival of delight, amazement, awe, deep gratitude to be alive.

This is what many of us wanted and thought we were going to get if we applied ourselves strongly enough, with enough gusto, and simply tapped enough.

We were wrong to have thought that we could do it that way.

And it wasn't that EFT couldn't do it.

We were using them not at all to their full potential because we were hamstrung by a deeply embedded, old, old, standard way of thinking about the nature of what holds someone's personality together and how it is shaped.

The Trauma Model

The presupposition which underlies all and every therapy form we ever had, is that at the moment of conception, a genetic being is created that is to all intents and purposes, perfectly well capable of being all that a human being can be.

Now, this perfect template gets "spoiled" by various traumas.

First it was childhood traumas, then it went to birth trauma, pre-birth trauma and then into past life trauma.

If we can find the source of the trauma, we can release it and all will be well.

That's the theory. Only, for a great many of the transformational blockages no trauma could be found in memory, or if something that might fit the bill was discovered, it was treated and emotions were released but it didn't change the presenting problem group.

Let's be quite clear about it here - I am not talking about a spider phobia, one event sets up a clear response that is only present in the presence of spiders. I am talking about wide ranging, wide reaching self identity issues that just wouldn't shift no matter how much was tapped, and even less so in spite of thousands of repeated affirmations being "rubbed in".

Then there were the Gate Keepers - memories that would turn up over and over again in the context of one or more presenting problems, no matter how much tapping someone did on them, until the time came when the owner of the Gate Keeper memory simply gave up the ghost and stopped trying to do anything else with that particular memory as it absolutely would not resolve.

So the quest for trauma - and the idea being, that the more severe the presenting pathology or symptoms, the more severe the trauma must have been - went on and through all the fields of psychology, never questioned, always pre-supposed, because it did work in some cases, in most cases, and especially in most cases where there was a directly observable behavioural component to the problem and cognition of the problem.

What I have found is that trauma only accounts for half of the problem, and that indeed, trauma is not the only life setting, time line programming, belief and value forming force we had thought it to be. Indeed, it is actually very rarely so and rarely so by itself.

There is another component to the puzzle that is a far more powerful factor in shaping someone's life into a specific direction with intense force, intensely long lasting, and the repercussions of which are so wide ranging, it is absolutely extraordinary. What could that component possibly be?

Understanding "Trauma"

What does that word, trauma, actually mean?

In psychology (which includes all sorts of mind healing techniques and systems in my definition, including hypnosis, NLP, counselling, etc) trauma refers to a negative experience that had a very high "emotional charge" attached to it.

"Something" happens in a person's neurology when such a charge is unleashed - in some fields, this is described as a "significant emotional experience (SEE)".

Trauma or a negative SEE can be very dangerous to the systems of the mind, so there are little understood structures in place to safeguard the mind and to encapsulate the memories that carry the high charges, to keep them from spreading across the neurology - from the formation of "parts", simple subroutines that function independently and context specific outside of someone's conscious awareness, to deep repression and all the way to splitting off into multiple personalities (MPD or DID).

Now I won't even attempt to get scientific on these processes, because in spite of the hundreds of thousands of words - and many of them very important sounding indeed - that have been written on the subject, no-one has any idea of how this really works on all levels; yet we do know this process exists because we have observed it in action and the SEE/trauma model is a good explanation for how someone simply cannot recall that they had been raped at all, or how DID comes to be.

The quest to discover and correct trauma has led to ever more complex protocols, designed to root them out; and as these ever more complex protocols of course and by their very nature, chunk down lower and lower and then lower still, they also have an unfortunate tendency to become less effective as they go.

Others have turned to look at other, probably hitherto undiscovered countries of potential trauma/SEE sources, such as Munchausen By Proxy syndrome (which is far more wide spread amongst parents than you would ever believe) or Passive Aggressive Child Abuse. These and many of the other avenues are all worthwhile to explore, and I do know that we will find many more of such "trauma countries" as we continue to look for the reasons of adult behaviour and seek to understand the workings of our minds across our times of lives.

These patterns of abuse and trauma do indeed, form a network of interconnected structures that help to hold an individual's personality and behaviour together across time, but the one thing we never really thought about properly was the effect of **Positive Significant Emotional Experiences** nor did we seek to correct their effects on the neurology, and thus, on a person's life.

There's so little love as it is ...

The very first time I came across the possibility that the driver behind a major destructive behaviour was a positive memory rather than a negative one was a lady, let's call her Sandy, who was life-threateningly overweight yet continued to eat ice cream, and especially strawberry ice cream, by the bucket load.

I mean this quite literally. She bought wholesale buckets and had a special freezer that would take them.

When we applied EFT to the strawberry ice cream as a matter of fact approach to reducing the cravings, she became intensely "resistant" because a memory flashed up which was as follows:

She is 7 years old and it is high summer. She is, unusually, on a beach with her father who worked all the time and never took holidays. Her father buys her a strawberry ice cream and they both sit next to each other on a bench.

He puts his arm around her, awkwardly, and for the first and ONLY time in her entire childhood, she feels as though her father loves her.

The client cried heartbrokenly and begged me not to remove the memory.

"Please," she said, "If you take this from me, what will I have left?"

I listened to her and did, therefore, other things instead. I backed up on attempting to take the emotional charge of that memory or work on it in any other way and I thereby did that client the most profound disservice I could have possibly done.

However, at that time I did not know what I know now, and although the memory of this particular client kept haunting me and nudging at my awareness, and I even posted it to a few lists, I continued to behave like the nicely entrained little maze running creature that I used to be and kept questing for negative forms of trauma and trauma based significant emotional experiences.

Eventually, I forgot all about Sandy and her strawberry ice cream.

Until 18 months later, I was doing an intervention with a client who had so many symptoms that you could have split her up into about a hundred separate case histories. All kinds of things. I was working with her long term and open ended, because between the two of us we must have decided at some point that obviously her problems were such that we would just have to keep on tapping and crying and releasing one thing after the other until the stars fell from the heavens.

To be sure, it was fun on a level and we both looked forward to our weekly sessions of emotional drama and had many, many learnings about many, many things along the way. During a recent one of these many sessions, where I was giving my unconscious mind free range and just let it do whatever it liked by the way of which points to tap, which if any MET to use, which topic to address and how to go about it, we ended up doing a Grovian style metaphor intervention on a particular body sensation.

The lady flashed up a memory from nowhere of a time when she had been on holiday with her husband and son, aged 3, at the seaside.

It was profoundly emotional, profoundly moving, and in flavour eerily similar to the ice cream experience which I remembered immediately and which caused a shiver to go down my back.

This time, I made the client tap on it.

Yes, I **made her** tap on it because she, too, didn't want to release the intense emotion of love and connectedness for her family, her unique feeling of actually being able to be a good mother and a good wife, which she had not experienced before and would never experience again in all the years that followed.

The memory flash occurred whilst we were tapping the eliciting metaphor, and we were still in a tapping round and I had her continue to tap the eye points as she told me about the memory.

She said, frightened and as an aside, "This won't destroy that memory, will it?" and I remember clearly saying to her, "Under the eye now: It was the best day of my life."

The client followed suit and did it, we tapped on the collarbone point and then, all hell broke loose.

She began to literally howl and cry and scream and I had a job to be able to keep tapping her and all I could think to say was to repeat the NLP style encouragement and centring phrase of, "You're doing really, really well. You're doing well. You're doing a good job." until she subsided.

What she told me after that absolutely blew me away.

She had had the following insights which had caused the extreme emotional abreaction following the tapping on the "happy" memory:

- It became clear to her that she had tried to unconsciously re-create the memory in reality for the past 16 years.

- This attempt at re-creating the memory went as specific and as far reaching as to have the husband always (at the dining table, in the sitting room, in the car, wherever they ever went and whatever they ever did) at the left, and the son on the right.

- In the memory, the son wore a blue T-shirt. She had bought him nothing but blue clothes of that hue or near enough until he was old enough to start fighting against this, and still to this day, blue clothing was a really sore point between them

- He never, ever wore blue now and it caused her considerable distress.

- She had engineered their lives so that the husband no longer went out to work but was at home, and the son was at home too and not attending school.

- She could not sell the house by the seaside they had bought immediately after that holiday although it would have been long appropriate to do so. She could not bear the thought.

- The attempts at re-creating the feeling of that holiday had caused unbearable conflict between her and her son, and everyone was always accusing her of "treating him like a three year old", which indeed, she was trying to achieve with every resource that she had at her disposal: behaviourally, psychologically, energetically, practically and most of all - unconsciously.

- The conflicts and feelings of desperation about her inability to be a good wife and mother were getting worse with each passing year as hope to re-create this one moment in time was fading further and further away, yet the memory itself did not fade one bit.

And finally, and most horrendously of all:

- Her very attempts of re-creating the scene and the feelings of that one moment in time **had effectively precluded any further experiences of a similar nature for the intervening 16 years.**

All of this, and the interrelationships between that one event and a whole host of most horrendously wide ranging disturbances that she had been entirely unable to resolve through so much therapy, came to her in a single blinding flash of insight.

When it came, it caused her to experience a huge shock of emotional pain - guilt, horror, terror, loss of life, responsibility for what she had done to herself and her family - that caused the abreaction and what I could see in front of me.

I conducted further treatments and gave the lady a great deal of supportive talk and suggestions but it still was about an hour later until she was well enough to leave my office.

Half an hour later, I received a telephone call from her. She rang me to tell me that she had just realised that she had a photograph, taken on that very holiday, framed on the landing so you could see it every single time you came into the house or walked up the stairs.

To be honest with you, dear reader, I was in shock following this treatment. Whilst the client was abreacting, I had tracked across my mind to my greatest moment of my life, which had occurred approximately ten years ago.

It was the morning after the birth of my child, and I was in bed, feeling deeply comfortable, with the baby at my breast, looking out at a bright blue autumn sky and for the first time ever, I felt at peace, happy, and as though I could actually love at all and that I had done one thing right and had a right to be on this planet - a feeling of such love and connectedness swept over me, I do simply not have the words to describe it. I remember clearly standing in the office when the same shock of realisation that had hit my client, hit me.

It was like a physical force striking me in the back, causing me to go down on my knees and tears to fly horizontally from my eyes in an instant as the weight of unbelievable guilt for what **I** had done to **my child** and **both our lives** as a result of that one happy memory.

Ladies and gentlemen, I cannot, in truth, describe to you what that felt like to understand.

I didn't howl like my client had done earlier that day, but I thought I was going to choke on my own guilt, physically, and really couldn't breathe properly for a long, long time.

When I managed to pick myself up enough to crawl to the phone and call a fellow therapist, and in spite of my own mental state, I knew already that here we had found something that would change lives more profoundly than any tapping on childhood trauma for months on end could.

- The happy memories guarded an entire hornet's nest of awful things.

- The happy memories caused - directly! - seemingly irrational and intensely destructive behaviour that was entirely unconscious and entirely cohesive and entirely of single-minded congruency in its volition and aims.

- The happy memories were at the root core of what appeared to be blatant self sabotage and identity reversals.

- The happy memories provided the glue that was holding our lives together and gave it shape, form, function and **direction** all at the same time.

- The happy memories shaped life to their own image at all levels, in all ways, causing more and more tension and destruction the further they went in time from the state of being then and to how it was right now

This **WAS ABSOLUTELY** the famous Miss Haversham from Dickens's Great Expectations, who sat forty years later in her tattered and moth eaten wedding dress, **her life ruled by a single moment that once was and could never be again**, yet being entirely powerless to even take the decomposed wedding cake off the table.

It was truly frightening and yet truly enlightening as to how things work in the real world and why we have to take a step into a greater universe where lives are not just shaped by trauma, but quite in the contrary, **by single flares of moments of love, of connectedness and of glory.**

The Genesis of A Guiding Star

Here is my visualisation to explain what happens:

These single moments of holy and transpersonal joy, moments of what I would call a "revelation" and in general psychology literature are referred to as "epiphanic moments" have such a high emotional charge behind them that they launch right up into high orbit, above and detached from the normal functioning of the thought processes, and sit above a person's time line, outside of time itself, and provide the Guiding Star by which a person's life is shaped.

With them, they take the whole gestalt of trauma of that topic and seal it behind themselves so it becomes invisible, thus actually functioning as a Gate Keeper in structure, and this is of course why the abreactions are so furious.

Our unconscious mind, which contrary to public opinion does not seek to punish us or destroy us because our self concepts are so terrible, but quite in the opposite, will do anything it can to make us feel that happy again, sets the course towards the Guiding Star, and actively tries to bring it about so it may be re-experienced with every single resource it has at its disposal.

If, say a personal trainer went to see Miss Haversham, and gave her a good talking to along the lines of, "Now come on, there's so much more out there, you're still a fine looking woman, get that damned wedding dress off, sell this junk heap to the property developers, get a nice bungalow and join a dating agency!", it is possible that consciously, Miss Haversham would see the sense in that and make a real fist-on-the-table decision:

"Yes! You're right! I'm gonna make the change! I'll start today!"

But what happens is that she is planning a time line that is at right angles to the direction of her Guiding Star which insists on that this happiness can only be re-experienced if the house is the same, the dress is the same, in fact everything is exactly as it had been all those years ago.

The Guiding Star mechanisms will make sure that things counter to its intentions will not come to pass.

As Miss Haversham phones the newspaper to place an advertisement for her house, she may "forget" a digit or dictate a wrong one, so that no-one comes to call; or she may find a whole host of "very rational reasons" as to why exactly it would be unwise, illogical, downright stupid to sell the house in the falling market and it would be so much better to wait a while longer ...

Piece by piece, and bit by bit, surreptitiously and entirely outside the conscious awareness, the ship that is Miss Haversham on her special time line beneath that Guiding Star will be brought back on track.

The more difference between an individual's conscious choices, and the Guiding Star, the greater the tension becomes as the unconscious tries to pull us right back onto track; and if it has to, our unconscious mind will create disasters, accidents, illness to make sure that tension is released and we are back where we should be, where it feels right and good to be, no matter how obviously painful the lives we are leading have become as a result of these bizarre behavioural choices that make no sense to anyone other than the one who is guided by their own extra special Guiding Stars.

It is my contention that Guiding Stars can only be removed as directional devices (prior to doing this deliberately, of course!) by another (positive OR negative) significant emotional experience that is higher in intensity than the original Guiding Star experience was.

When that happens, the alcoholic will wake up one morning and decide that they have suffered enough and they will be able to make the changes requisite to follow a new and different path.

And the funny thing is, that we already know all these things unconsciously, just like Mr Dickens understood full well what the Miss Havershams of this world were doing.

A young lady who had been beaten terribly by her husband yet again said to me when asked why she wasn't leaving him, "It hasn't been bad enough yet."

General Observations On The Guiding Stars

A most fascinating feature of the Guiding Star mechanism is how whatever the topic might be, it takes the entire set of traumatic gestalts into orbit along with itself at the same time and thus makes the gestalt essentially unreachable, or perhaps I should say, it hides that nest of worms in a place where therapists simply haven't thought to look, hamstrung as we were whilst working with the Trauma Only model.

It truly is astonishing how our unconscious minds and our neurological processes will endeavour to take lemons and to turn them into lemonade for us.

It is my supposition that this simple understanding will help alleviate a lot of paranoia and internal conflict to those who have long suspected their unconscious minds to be the equivalent of a nasty lurking monster under the coffee table, waiting to pounce out on us and destroy any hope of happiness we might ever get to possess!

Also, big problems arise when a person's own Guiding Stars are at conflict with each other and try to plot alternative courses. You can see this behaviourally and practically with simultaneous and sequential incongruencies in people - their lives might really and truthfully look like a zigzag course between polar opposites, with tension either way that can never be resolved.

That's where parts conflicts come from, and at the highest end, multiple personality disorder where the body takes turns to follow separate Guiding Stars.

The Guiding Star memories themselves have something in common with high trauma and yet there's something very important that they do not have in common.

Guiding Stars are not repressed but available as a resource throughout a person's lifetime. If you have ever been around old people for any length of time, they will tell you clearly their Guiding Stars and refer to the same ones over and over again - sometimes only a single one they will keep repeating.

In moments of despair, doubt, unhappiness etc., the Guiding Star memory is there to fall back upon - and this is both a blessing for the moment as well as an absolute nightmare for the here-and-now, as we will discuss in some detail later on.

One thing that they do share with serious high end trauma memories is firstly, that they are outside the normal memory/state systems and secondly and probably because of it, that they are fixed and frozen in time and space.

To take an example, a person who is being raped might generally experience a deep disassociation - their mind leaves their body, as it is

142

called, or a part of their personality splits off, or there is soul loss, or in ERP talk, a part of their energetic self goes into high orbit and becomes unavailable from thereon in.

This memory becomes encapsulated and detached from the rest of the awareness and David Grove, who I would like to give a brief bow to with respect for his work and understanding of the subject, points out that there are two things about this splitting off process that causes the major long term damage:

Firstly, the real horrible event the person is so afraid of, **never actually happens at all** because cognition is shut off before we get to this point.

So, a person who falls from a window never hits the ground; the oncoming car never actually impacts with your body; and the torture victim never did break and give up the name of their fellow conspirators.

This means that the event and all its repercussions can never be processed properly and the normal flow of emotions and physical sensations is wildly disrupted; the lessons can't be learned, and in the case of the spy, although he knows well that he must have given up the people's names in consciousness, he feels blameless and guiltless and cannot begin to accept responsibility for the effects of his actions, nor ever reconcile his own self concept with reality at all, which is a most dangerous and disruptive place to be.

The second side effect of the encapsulation that occurs before the main event is that there is a bubble floating around in the neurology where the man is always and continuously falling from the window for eternity, the woman on the road is standing in the headlights forever and the terrible pain the spy is experiencing has never stopped at all.

This causes serious disruptions (injuries or open sores) on the energetic level and is often expressed the only way these things are expressed: through the physiology, and at the general conscious level, perhaps in traces and hints of disturbing dreams, but never available to literary cognitive consciousness.

Similarly, Guiding Star memories are frozen thus in time and space. A split occurs too, but this is a split off into transpersonal levels, highly charged energetic realms where the joy of life resides most bountifully.

The encapsulation also occurs, and like with the trauma memories, **time stands still inside the memory** (and it really is usually a single space-time point snapshot which contains the instantaneous revelation rush) and it never ends, either.

We are really talking about the equivalent of a multi-dimensional "mental photograph" that provides the template, complete with circumstances, background AND (very importantly!!) a map of the individual's body and body states at the time.

If you wish, you could now wonder how your predilection for certain items or styles of clothing came about, or how you know to like certain foods so much, or certain body types of certain people.

The Guiding Stars paradigm explain a whole lot of things.

Here are just a few at random:

- Little girls and little boys **do not go out of their way** to marry their mums and dads by choosing similar people - energetically speaking. If they do, it's because there has been usually **a single revelation incident** of feeling deeply loved, appreciated and accepted and loving mummy or daddy in fullness in return. The Guiding Star Snapshot is born.

- Following on from this, women who, for example, always marry alcoholics are **not** deranged masochists who hate themselves for their low self concepts and seek punishment. Quite on the contrary. Chances are there was this one time when daddy came home, reeling and reeking of alcohol, picked up the little girl, sat her on his lap and called her "My beautiful princess". **THAT** moment, **THAT** feeling is what they're trying to recreate - and not all the years of constant and daily abuse!

- Women under a Guiding Star of a man who is angry and hits women, similarly, have a terrifying struggle on their hands when well meaning care workers walk in and tell them all the rational reasons as to why they should pack up and go to the women's shelter, always with the tutted pre-supposition right behind their kindly words that the woman is intensely stupid for still being with this guy. That sets up the tension conflict with their Guiding Star which may have been with daddy or even the abusive man himself, and leads to an absolutely shattering experience when they finally "give in" under the threat of death or harm to their children and "abandon their Guiding Star".

- Abandoning your Guiding Star is one of the worst experiences in a person's life time. It is such a crushing of hope "that there will ever be any moment of happiness for me, ever, in this life time" that it can literally kill people. As not a single person I can conceive of has a Guiding Star that leads to them sitting alone and abandoned in an old' people's home (although they may fear this!), this is a good explanation why the survival rate in those homes is so abysmal in comparison to old folk living at home or with a family.

We will do anything at all to prevent that moment of the Guiding Star falling.

We will hallucinate, pretend, see things differently in the mirror, ignore, re-frame, re-interpret - **anything at all to safeguard this treasure, the wonder that is the Guiding Star.**

Now, consider for a moment what happens on all levels to an individual...

... when you release that Guiding Star and restore the memory to its rightful place in the time line, in the past where it belongs, where its learnings and understandings are needed on so many levels, and where it no longer warps the path an individual has to take through the world?

How To Release The Guiding Stars

EFT *could* be used to remove the emotional content from Guiding Stars just as well as they remove it from the deepest, darkest Trauma by healing the underlying "energetic disturbance".

Let us remember Sandy, the lady who loved Strawberry Ice-cream so much that she was willing to jeopardise, if not sacrifice, her own life in the name of that love.

She said, "If you take that memory from me, what will I have left?"

And the answer to that question, painfully, is the acknowledgement of a veritable wasteland of a life of unlived dreams, missed opportunities, horrible catastrophes visited upon self and others in the name of the Guiding Star.

It is realisation and guilt and grief of unprecedented proportions, and the longer the Guiding Star stood above the individual life, the worse this is.

This is such a specific process that I really had never encountered before I began to apply METs to deep structural issues that I gave it a name.

Loss Of Life

I called it "Loss Of Life."

"Loss Of Life" is terrible in and of itself, but especially so when:

- o **you cannot make up for what you have done to yourself;**
- o **you cannot make up for what you have done to others;**
- o **and the time has passed to do anything at all to put the past to rights in physical terms.**

For example, a woman over fifty cannot ever have a child, even if she now recognises that the only reason that she did not was a Guiding Star moment from her earliest childhood that demanded this within its own context.

EFT Opening Statement Suggestions for Loss Of Life:

- What has been, has been.
- What is done, is done.
- I choose the future.
- I always did my best.

What Has Been, Has Been

For some people, their victims and their children have long grown up and their childhoods are irretrievably lost; even worse if it was their sanity that was lost, or even their lives.

So, that sounds pretty bad, doesn't it?

Here, let me take your best memories and instead, you can experience your own personal hell and dark night of the soul - in minutes if not seconds, thanks to Meridian Energy Therapies and a Guiding Stars specialist!

Indeed, one should choose to whom such a treatment is offered to with some care and concern for ecology and entirely based on the circumstances of the individual and their relationship with themselves and/or their therapist.

Simply put, you can drive people to suicide with this pattern.

Please note that I don't mean the above sentence metaphorically or say it lightly.

I know of an incident, many years ago to illustrate this clearly. A young man who had experienced a Guiding Star moment with an abuser left the office of a (non-EFT-enabled) social worker who had inadvertently "shot it down" in an effort to get him to testify against his abuser in court by telling him congruently that the abuser had "set him up deliberately" and that "all he felt at that time was a delusion".

This young man never went home. He walked across town to the site of the guiding star incident and there, he threw himself off a 60 foot high motorway bridge into the traffic below.

When you work with this pattern, it is essential to **respect the experience** and not just respect but to honour it, treasure and celebrate it.

It is quite right that people say it was magical, truly holy.

It left an indelible **impression** upon them and all their systems.

A Guiding Star experience is absolutely **an enlightenment experience** that needs to be treated with wonder, reverence and with greatest care.

The repercussions these experiences had as they were being misinterpreted in consciousness are nothing but a **terrible side effect** of a natural and most wonderful system which is clearly designed to **have us seek out these kinds of experiences** throughout our lives.

If the social worker had known to have the young man understand that he was not deluded when he felt truly loved and accepted at that moment but indeed, he **did** feel that, and in feeling that, should have learned nothing more than **he can feel LIKE THAT** and all the other things are not important in comparison, he could have well coped with the loss of life this Guiding Star moment brought about in its wake.

How can something so beautiful have such perverted results and these extraordinary negative repercussions?

That is a difficult question, and we might do well to consider this for the future.

In the meantime, let us look on the bright side - and this is a bright side indeed, for it offers us hope on a scale we have really not experienced before:

However much life or however little life there is left to be lived, once the entanglements around the Guiding Star are no longer blocking the process of life itself and blind an individual to all the myriad possibilities to have more, other, richer, righter, different and even more in depth experiences, the universe is once more at your finger tips.

If a person can make it past the initial rush of guilt and horror, it opens the door wide to a deep healing and personal transformation at an unprecedented level.

It will unlock an understanding of your own self that is truly extraordinary, and it immediately and instantly, sets all those bound by you and your Guiding Star through energetic entanglements, free to do their own thing as well.

I have no idea if that even applies to those who have died in the course of the time spent beneath the Guiding Star, but it is certainly a consideration to offer to those who have revelations concerning those who are no longer alive, such as their parents, friends who committed suicide, or their children.

The above is what happens with mature and older people. Interestingly, when applied closer to formation and without so much time spent in the prison beneath the Guiding Star, it is much more profoundly and immediately useful.

As one of my test clients, a 25 year old man who was sexually abused all through his childhood, said to me following a Guiding Star intervention:

"You cannot begin to know what you have done for me today. You cannot begin to understand the relief I feel and the total joy at not having to become one of them. It stops right here, this minute, with me. I can feel it in every part of me - such freedom. I don't have to become that, I can end it. I can be free."

That is in the context of child abuse. Since the Guiding Star treatment, this particular man has reported complete cessation of paedophilic impulses that were making his life a desperate hell and which had not been alleviated by tapping on the negative traumas he sustained.

To me, what is more valuable than anything is the insight that **our unconscious minds were not ever sabotaging us at all**. We were not living with an invisible enemy strangling the joy from our lives but a system that is designed to help us know what makes us truly happy so we can find more of the same.

Now, some practical considerations as to the treatments and strategies employed.

Locating A Guiding Star

To find a relevant Guiding Star is actually very easy. The client knows them very well, very intimately. They may or may not be willing to share them with you on the grounds that they are holy, sacrosanct and exclusively theirs. It depends on the level of rapport you can achieve with a client as to whether they will tell you what they are.

If they won't/can't tell you, it matters not. I just talk and tell them about how it works, tell the story of the lady on the beach with her family and what happened to her, my own experience with it, much as I've told you today.

Clients cannot help but draw their own parallels as you are speaking.

If the client won't or can't progress from there, I leave it with them as a thought and offer to work on any aspect of the insights and new understandings this has produced. I always make sure they are familiar with the basic EFT protocol as well as an "emergency point procedure" should they experience anything in a place where they need rapid relief from unwanted memories, flashbacks, insights into further repercussions and overwhelm.

It is also and totally absolutely the client's right to keep their Guiding Star systems intact and have them remain as they always were.

Please bear in mind that this is a serious, SERIOUS issue and a serious intervention that must never be undertaken lightly. It changes people profoundly to remove the entanglements they have with their Guiding Stars and can and does cause absolute chaos in their ecology - both mental as well as very practically as all their existing relationships with all the people in their lives might well be based on, and around, one particular major Guiding Star, the corresponding energetic entanglements and many, many false equivalencies, beliefs and even life long values are all based on what happened neurologically in the aftermath of a Guiding Star experience.

Don't Treat The Star, Treat THE MEANINGS

When first this protocol was discovered and conceived of, we made the mistake of treating the Guiding Stars directly - i.e. tapping the emotion from it. This was based on a major misunderstanding of the nature of these experiences and also with hindsight an ecological disaster although, as many such interventions are, conducted in good faith and the desire to "set the client free".

The Guiding Stars are very important in a person's life and not to have any left, means to have missed just about the whole point of why we should be alive at all.

It turns out that the problem with the Guiding Stars was not their emotional content at all - there is nothing wrong with feeling profound love, profound connection and profound happiness, indeed! - but the meanings the person made from this.

A Guiding Star experience is NOT like a trauma in that sense. Yes, it impacts the energy body profoundly and changes it instantly but this is actually **a change for the better** if only we knew it.

"Healing" these energetic changes and putting things back to how they were before is like surgically removing a magical third eye that has suddenly appeared in your forehead because it is being mistaken for some form of melanoma.

Life Destroying Meanings

I use the term "meanings" as a global collective device to cover all forms of directional neurological events - you can call them "decisions", "realisations", "discovering the truth" - they are the bit at the end of the equivalence sign in our neurology.

Much more than just mere words, these meanings that people make automatically from their unique experiences are directive devices that prejudice thought, feeling, behaviour into a specific mode of interpreting the events and to store them, use them as a base for making decisions and to make further meanings which then result in specific behaviour.

In NLP, these constructs are referred to as "maps" and when someone engages in unhealthy behaviour, it is supposed that there is a flaw in the map. In my terminology, I say that a person has made unhelpful meanings or **drawn the wrong conclusions from their experiences** - wrong in the sense of that when challenged, they are not the only possible conclusion one could have drawn from the experience, and that they are generally not the most productive ones.

For example, the ice cream lady had made meanings such as, "I can only feel my father's love in the presence of strawberry ice cream."

Such a mistake is easy to make, especially for a child but also for anyone quite automatically - the beach lady made the meaning of "My child has to wear blue clothes and must never grow up." from her experience.

These kinds of meanings, however, are actually secondary to the really destructive ones below all of that detail.

Why, for example, would someone immediately presume that this is as good as it gets rather than to think of the experience as a first taste of what there can be had in the way of feeling absolutely wonderful, the first introduction to an entire world of bright new states of being?

I believe that the reason this happens is because there has been so little in the way of numinosity in people's lives up to the point of the Guiding Star event, it just blows their neurology out of the water - there is no step stoning, there is no preparation, it's a straight catapulting into areas of emotions, feelings and sensations that were never even dreamed of, that the person never even thought could possibly exist.

As it is so rare and unprecedented, probably entirely unmodelled by others around them, completely outside their "normal" range of functioning and even expectation, it is easy to make the worst possible meanings you could make of a Guiding Star event, for example the oft repeated,

"This IS the best moment of my life."

Here are some other meanings that have the power to end further happiness in an instant:

- "It can never get any better than this."

- "This is the moment I have been waiting for my entire life."

- "This is the only time and place I would ever want to be."

- "This is it."

- "This is my one moment of grace."

- "I will never experience anything like this again."

- "This is so far beyond any feeling I ever knew before, it must be all there is, all there could ever be."

- "I can never be as happy as this, ever again."

- "I wish it would be like this, forever."

Stop for a moment and consider the repercussions of these statements, given as a direct instruction to your own neurology with the intense power of those emotions behind them.

It is literally frightening because it entirely presupposes that it simply can't get any better than this.

No wonder that the neurology tries to recreate the events so endlessly, and with such desperate measures!

It is these "false meanings" that are nasty rubber band-like energetic occurrences and which distort a person's life, not the experience in and of itself which "was as it was" and in fact, actually represents a fantastic resource, once the meanings have been removed and it is once again,

152

allowed to return to what it really was - a new experience that showed a person **how much more there was** than they previously came to believe or even hope for.

Discovering the false meanings and releasing the client from these is an excellent healing process that is profoundly moving, profoundly useful, and deeply beneficial to the client.

All the above "life killing decisions" are great candidates for opening statements and set ups when treating the Guiding Stars meanings. As always, we use the client's own words exactly as they said them:

"Even though I think it can never get any better than that, I deeply and profoundly love and accept myself", for example.

False Ties & Crystalline Constructs

If you remember, we noted earlier that the Guiding Star moment creates a neurological "snapshot" of **everything** that was present at the time – people, places, weather, objects, colours, creatures, and their own body as well.

Indeed, it is the greatest catastrophe of the Guiding Stars experiences that we fail to understand that **the experience was not reliant on any one of the components** which were present at the time.

Sometimes, it seems the whole universe conspires to create "a magic moment" – and you know, it can happen anywhere, everywhere, randomly, any time. You could say all the energetic components of everything that was there for **one single moment in time** aligned all of a sudden and in that moment, there was the breakthrough into magic for the individual who experienced it.

People try to re-create these magic moments endlessly in a quest to re-experience this magic. Many more try to experience them for the first time, setting the scene, for example for a romantic get away or a family Christmas dinner with excruciating care to make sure that they will get "all the details just exactly right" to help create **the state of magic**.

And that is what it is – it is a **state of being** in which you can all of a sudden **feel the magic that is actually there all the time** if only you knew it, or **if you could access this state of being**.

All the people, objects, environments, rose petals strewn on the bed, the partner in question (yes, that too), the music, the time of year are not the **cause** of feeling that good at all but it is in fact an individual's own state of receptivity and being that is the cause – **opening to the magic for a split second and seeing what is really there in the world.**

For the treatment of problem sets where Guiding Star moments have become completely mis-interpreted it is absolutely essential that the external circumstances be returned to what they were – props rather than the cause of what happened.

When you do this, the individual becomes free to experiment with trying to reach that **state of being** in other circumstances, with different partners, regardless of the weather, regardless how old they are, regardless of where they happen to find themselves in the World at any point in space or time.

Of course and as direct effect, this will also set the individual free from their pathological **ties** to certain people, certain types of people, objects, substances and so much more.

Here are a few examples of opening statements for removing these unrealistic ties:

- "Even though I thought I could only feel like that with (x), ..."
- "Even though I believe that only (x) can make me feel that way ..."
- "Even though I can only feel like that when I'm (x) ..."
- "Even though I think I need (x) to feel like that again ..."
- "Even though I am terrified that if I don't have (x) I can never feel like that again ..."

It might be interesting to note that in order to actively **create** a Guiding Star type experience how very important it is to not just have the setting, the actors and the props all in the perfect alignment, but to give much more thought as to how to encourage the people present into **a state of being** where magic is simply, the natural order of things and all around us.

EFT Treatments For Guiding Stars Issues

Using SLOW EFT for Guiding Star Related Issues

SLOW is a very thorough protocol that really cleans up energetic entanglements over a vast range of gestalts.

Help the client develop a keyword for the Guiding Star Issues in their totality - both the good and the repercussions, the love and the suffering, all of it together in one overarching metaphor.

Have the client speak the word and gently treat one point at the time, including extra points as you see fit.

With sweeping GS gestalts, suggest the client to do it in homework, one point per day, to not further overload the system and give the client time to adjust.

TAT Treatments For Guiding Stars

Although this is explicitly an EFT manual, for the sake of the clients I feel honour bound to bring in TAT (Tapas Acupressure Technique) at this point as there is no equivalent EFT protocol to create the effects of the TAT head-hold posture for moments of stress and deep overwhelm.

This is one of these times when bringing in words is bound to be a severe hindrance rather than a help.

The Guiding Star experiences are by nature, transpersonal, numinous, epiphanic, extraordinary - well, as you can see, words rather fail us there. The emotions experienced, likewise, defy ordinary labelling.

It's not just "happy" it is "happy+ + + + + +" what we are dealing with.

So we turn to silence instead.

Simply instruct the client to hold the basic TAT posture whilst contemplating the memory, and more specifically, to look at and to tune into that multidimensional snap shot that is the highlight of the experience, or whichever way they usually "think about" that experience.

Remind them to breathe and have them talk if it's appropriate as to what's happening inside their minds and bodies as they do this.

I also send a general vibration of acceptance, steadying and moral support whilst this is going on, and might interject a low, "You're doing very well", if their courage seems to falter.

The Guiding Stars Abreaction

Sooner or later, you might or might not have a serious abreaction in the client. That's the moment when it really "hits them" what has been going on with their lives since the inception of the Guiding Star and the meanings that were derived there.

It is an indication that the snap shot memory has become re-connected to the general system and the mental landscape that was focussed on the snap shot now opens out far and wide - remember the longer it has been going on, the more there is to it, and the more profound the abreaction is likely to be.

- Stay with the client, hold their hand, tap them or yourself or simply be there with steadying support, depending on the client, until they have subsided and can talk again.

- Don't try to have them make sense at this point or tell them anything complicated.

- They are re-processing at a furious rate all across their neurology and will need gentle support to bring them back.

- Let them say what they want or if they are not speaking, leave them there and silently work on their energy system with support, respect to their experience, and general gentling.

- You can do this via imaginary tapping, sending them colours, a "Gift", an imaginary TAT pose over their heads or anything that springs to mind and is appropriate to your ways of working with a client.

- You can borrow the basic "flow suggestions" from EmoTrance™ during this time – "What you are feeling are powerful energies shifting and re-aligning. Keep breathing and let these energies flow, find their own path, keep calmly breathing and let these energies flow out, back to the universe where they belong."

- As you are tapping or treating them, remember to steady them to you in the here-and-now. Keep talking calmly and steadily so they have something to hold on to. The basic instruction of "You are doing very well. Very good. That's right, let it flow and re-organise itself as we heal these injuries, you are doing very well ..." repeated over and over again will help the client tremendously and guide them back to a steadier state reliably.

When the abreaction is beginning to abate in waves and for a considerable time afterwards, do nothing but help the client steady and centre in themselves.

You MUST give them all the time they need to regain clarity and focus; if another client is scheduled, you must cancel them. An abreaction is a major event that if treated wrongfully, aborted half way through the process or not properly seen back to a point of balance can lead to terrible damage.

I would also absolutely suggest an overall energy re-alignment for any client who has worked with their Guiding Stars in any shape or form. Please refer to the relevant section for strategies for overall re-alignments.

Discussing the Insights

This is vitally important to bridge between the unconscious shifts and re-organisations and conscious awareness, and also to have the client return to a state of being where they are reasonably safe to leave your office and get into their cars and you have some confidence that they will get home in one piece.

Usually, there is a whole host of both negative traumas and negative emotions unearthed that have accumulated because the client did know on some level they were doing something strange, bizarre, incomprehensible to themselves and others and all of these seem to crowd out once the effect of the Guiding Star system has become apparent.

It is helpful at this point to say to the client that this does not have to be resolved in Toto overnight or even within a day or two; to come to an acceptance of that what happened, has indeed happened, and to delay judgement on anything nor try to make sense of it all until things have become a great deal clearer with hindsight.

It can be very helpful if the client, the therapist or both tap gently all the way through talking about what has happened and what insights were derived.

Bringing The Magic Home

If you recall, I said that the Guiding Stars are far above and away from other memories - they are not connected with the person's life properly, only via the false meanings they made from it in a most unhealthy fashion. This is because the states of beings in which Guiding Stars are indeed, the order of human experience is on a different **strata** of the energy body altogether, a different country if you will and no roads lead in or out .

The following process keeps the memory intact and is designed to re-connect the memory backward and forward into their time line so we may bring its magic home and have it be real as a real part of their lives, rather than a far away something that isn't there as a resource and learning about love and what you can feel, who you can be, what you can know.

When you do this, you are making a pathway to similar experiences from that strata of enlightenment experiences. The more pathways a person can make **and travel**, the **easier** it becomes to enter these mystical states of being and experiencing the magic of this world – what a gift!

Reconnecting displaced trauma memories into someone's general life line is achieved in Grovian Metaphor therapy with the simple question:

"And what happens next?"

In general, the answer is that "Life Goes On!" which is what had been missing from the memory, keeping it so frozen in time and far away from all ordinary existence.

The lady at the seaside with her husband and son, for example, might say that we sat there for a while, being happy, and then my husband and son got up and played a game of beach ball and I watched them, being happy, and then we went back to the guest house.

To be connect to the past, we ask:

"And what happened before?"

The answer to that might be that they had a minor row in the car, parked it up, got the picnic basket, found a spot on the beach, sat down and then there was this moment of real happiness.

This also gives you and the client the opportunity to discover further "false meanings" so that by the time you're done, at least that one Star is shining brightly and fully available to them in all ways.

The Energetic Effects Of Freeing a Guiding Star Memory

Freed from all distorting meanings, presuppositions and all of that, and fully available as an essentially content free power source in someone's life, Guiding Stars are a profound generator of energy for life.

This extends not only to general mental functionings but right into every cell of the body; you can expect a wonderful increase in general energy, resistance to both thought and physical attacks on the respective immune systems as well as a general "aliveness" that stays with the client once this intervention has been successfully completed.

Further, it is my belief and personal experience that having the Guiding Star charge there and available in its pure form (as nature intended it, you might say) becomes once more a directional device - but this time not directional to certain people, situations, strawberry ice cream and beaches **but to the very act of being alive, being loved, being aware and present and being at home here in the World itself.**

That is a most wonderful process indeed.

It is, you might say, a direction that cannot lead anyone at all anywhere other than towards themselves, towards wholeness and towards Even Flow.

This is a taste of what there is - now go out and find new ways to get more of this, in new flavours, in new contexts and prepare to be just as surprised once more as you were back then when reality exceeded even your own capability for dreaming in that moment.

I believe it is **the most essential** aspect of Guiding Stars treatments to have the client really understand and appreciate this properly.

Without this understanding, people go home and of course, they are a wreck of guilt and pain of the past.

With this understanding, we are turning the focus **from the past to the future** where it rightfully belongs, and the future looks bright, indeed.

Now, The Future ...

The last part of the Guiding Stars protocol is a classic EFT test of the changes.

In the case of this protocol, the test consists of discussing what the future will be like, and how the client's expectations of the future have changed because of the re-alignments and releases that happened during the treatment session.

This will reveal missed meanings and other aspects that stand in the way still to make this treatment complete and profoundly life changing as it can be when it is used with care, deliberation and attention to both detail as well as the larger picture.

There should be a true "sunrise" feel about the new future – it is alright if this is with some trepidation for new things always cause us to be a little uncertain. You are looking for a sense of excitement and the client expressing this not only in their choice of words, but also in their body postures and their overall energy.

It is of course not always possible to reach this stage in a single session so do make sure your client is totally stable with where they are at before you let them leave your care.

However, when this entire protocol has been successfully completed, not only should the client really know the sunrise has now happened, but you, too, should feel a real energy of excitement and delight in turn inside your own body.

Guiding Stars Homework and Tidy Up

The completion of the protocol, as described before, is of course what would happen a hundred percent of the time in that mystical perfect world, far, far away from any of us at this time!

You need to be very aware of the client's state of being with this protocol.

It rattles the very foundation of who or what they thought they were (often for a very long time indeed) and this can be very frightening for people; the speed at which you can move through the treatment steps of course depends entirely on the feedback you receive from each individual client.

For example, if "time's up" and your client is still fuzzy or highly emotional, cancel the next one because you need to spend more time with them, right here, right now.

You might break state with a drink of water, change the topic of the conversation for a while and very helpful is to ask the client:

"What would be the one thought or emotion, if we released that now, that would allow you to find a state of peace and clarity?"

When the client has regained their balance, you can choose to remind them to use all or any of the Energy Therapy interventions we have mentioned - EFT for specific meanings and emotions in private, SLOW for central and complicated groups of feelings and emotions, TAT for collections of memories that flash from one to the other too fast to "name that emotion", and Instant EFT for use in public places or when it is not appropriate to enter a treatment session - as and if required and make sure to book telephone feed back sessions with the client right away.

You may also create Emergency STOP procedures and custom algorithms, if you feel your client needs it. If your client has strong physical reactions to their thoughts and emotions, you might also show them The Gentle Touch which is most effective with deep level problems stored at the physical level and which are not easily accessible in consciousness through words, thoughts or pictures.

With this treatment, it is vitally important that the client is not left alone with what might turn up for the next few days.

Some clients will really need to talk about what they have found out and chances are, there are not that many people in their circle of friends who would have the faintest idea what they are talking about, so be on stand by!

You should also have a face-to-face or full session within a week or ten days at the latest, no matter what, to clear up fall out from the session and to test the changes into the future, for there is bound to be a level of confusion in the absence of the original meanings assigned to the Guiding Star, as well as seemingly strange and unexpected behavioural changes.

Guiding Star EFT Self Treatment

Basically, it is much the same as the client protocol with the one exception that you don't have someone on hand to say, "It's alright, you're doing really well" when the sky falls on your current time line.

It is very hard indeed to have come this far and read all of the preceding without having already made some connections and insights of your own; and because of this, there is a possibility that it's not going to be quite as frightening as it was for those who didn't know and didn't expect it to be happening as it did.

Disclaimer - READ CAREFULLY

The Guiding Star Self Help Pattern is to be understood as offered for use by experimenting therapists ONLY who have access to one or more others who know about the pattern for feedback and support, should this become necessary. The Guiding Stars Protocol is absolutely NOT a self help pattern by nature.

The severity of emotional responses and near catastrophic re-alignments AND the repercussions on the ecology of a person and all their relationships that are possible from this pattern make it unsuitable for self help without knowledgeable back up.

It is further NOT intended to be used in any other context than that of Meridian Energy Therapies as the main stay to deal with the emotional responses the pattern seems to provoke as I have no confidence that standard psychology and psychotherapy interventions can handle this type of emotional intensity with anything approaching the respect and effectiveness it clearly deserves.

If you are in doubt, you must consult with your health care providers before entering into this protocol.

So with this disclaimer, here is the:

Guiding Stars Self Help Protocol

Step 1: Are you ready to make some major changes in your life?

If not, consider the fears and issues carefully and treat yourself for the objections if you choose to do so. Bear in mind that this is your life, and it's entirely up to you what you do with it. Further, you are not just "ok" you are absolutely perfect the way you are right now, and don't let anyone, ever, tell you otherwise.

Remember: *"The perfection of this plane lies in the imperfections of its inhabitants." LA*

Step 2

Find the memory, find the snap shot.

Take your time to look at it and consider that one moment in time, remember it fully.

Step 3

Find the meanings you've made from the memory.

Take your time over this, it is bound to be very emotional and sometimes truly frightening as the repercussions of the meanings on your life become apparent.

Begin to tap on the meanings ONLY and as soon as you become aware of them.

Step 4

This is where the gate opens and the insights come with the floods of emotions. Do what you can, don't panic and remember that it will indeed, go away again.

Also remember that you do not have to make sense of anything you experience at this point, this is really just getting the stuff out of the cupboard. Organising it, understanding it, finding connections between events or even labelling anything at all comes much later and when you're ready to do so.

Step 5

Sit quietly and think about what you have learned or call a friend. Continue to treat any meanings and follow on aspects that come up with EFT or Instant EFT; for overwhelm on a topic group choose SLOW or the Channel Clearer and if there's that flash-by effect of many memories all rolled into one, TAT's your best option.

For aspects that cause you physical pain, use EmoTrance™ if you know it, if you do not, use the EFT Body Protocol.

Step 6

Stop at some point and go for a walk or take a bath or something of that nature.

Beyond a certain point, obsessing about what you have learned does not a lot of good because you need a bit of time to integrate the flood of information in consciousness. I would also recommend talking to someone about it all.

Step 7

During the time that follows, next day etc., treat what comes up and prepare yourself for some rather interesting behavioural shifts and changes of the "what on Earth did I just do???" kind of nature.

Step 8

It would be nice to jot down some notes on what happened and what topics were covered because once it all integrates successfully, you'll not remember accurately what exactly went on.

Step 9

This is the best part of the Guiding Stars protocol, and it is about contemplating a whole new future that simply wasn't there before, not even as a hint or shimmer on the horizon. You can still find the few odd stray meanings that are getting in the way at this point, and it's important to deal with these as soon as you become aware of them.

There may be fears that need to be addressed, doubts, deservability issues (track the meanings to past events and release the meanings), and also resolution, punishment and crime issues of all kinds that will give you a logical next step to preparing for a future so bright, you'll really have to wear shades.

Step 10

Lastly, here is a step into realms beyond your own dreams and expectations. "Making a new picture of the future" may show up areas that are outside any given person's world view or ability to even imagine.

For example, someone who has no experience of any kind of successful relationship, either personally or having it modelled in their environment, will lack of course any reference point to aim towards something they don't even understand or can consciously know will exist for them at all.

For a starving child in a refugee camp, "total happiness" may take the form of a bowl of gruel that they don't have to share with anyone. There is nothing beyond for them to dream of or to even wish for - they have no experience in their world that could even give them a new dream of more or better.

In order to overcome this structural limitation, I have invented the Solus Device, a holographic place holder of something you know you don't know yet but you trust is there for you to have and know in the future.

For example, if someone has a future that does not involve a relationship which would support them, make them happier than they were before and is of a whole new order of connectedness, and there is a sense that such a thing would be a good thing to have in their future, you can ask the person to place, for now, a white, as yet undefined, shape into the position which would be occupied by a future partner, friend, or other human they would like to have be there but cannot imagine in any detail as yet.

The same goes for other manifestations, such as houses, family relationships, objects and even body image - all these can be consciously set in the form of these holographic place holders that keep the possibilities open and declare a person's intentions to have such things be part of their future, as well as their admission that they don't know yet what exact shape this part of their future will manifest in.

This is a particularly useful and helpful approach when the Guiding Star has strongly defined many goals and laid out a particular form of future.

When this guidance system has gone, the gaps in the ecology of the future plans become apparent; Solus Devices fill the gaps, keeping the system stable and allowing for a new and different, if yet unknown future, to be manifest.

Clearing Guilt - The Redemption Patterns

In Guiding Stars interventions it is very likely is that you might be left on some topics with the serious problem of the crimes - or sins, if you will - the individual has committed, even unwittingly.

Telling someone that "it wasn't your fault" doesn't actually wash much with people on the whole at a profound level; try killing a child accidentally whilst backing out of your drive and you will know what I mean.

Burdens of guilt and shame are a real problem and a real concern on many levels because they continue to **tie the individual into an event that is, energetically speaking, of the past and by doing so, it warps the present out of shape.**

For our purposes here, it is neither here nor there whether the person "deserves" to be thus warped by the way of a punishment for their evil doings - I would like to see if we as therapists might not for a time move into a position where we accept that we cannot judge anyone at all, regardless of what they did or did not do, simply because it's neither our place nor our function.

For an individual to be able to go forward toward the future and to stop punishing themselves and their loved ones over crimes committed long ago and irretrievably done, some form of resolution is required - you might even call it a re-so-Lucian.

I would offer the following step stone pattern of energetic occurrences which are natural to our neurology. The terms used are simply used because they are the best we have to describe a very real process that really does occur in these stages and have no "religious" connotations beyond this fact. Please replace them with different words if you or your client cannot accept them.

Awareness

The first step on the road to being clear of certain energetic entanglements and injuries within yourself is to have an awareness that there is, indeed, a problem in the first place.

In general life, to get such awarenesses or insights into yourself may have taken years of repeated feedback from your body, your loved ones and the Universe itself in the form of knocks and bad luck.

When you are working with the Guiding Star protocol, these awarenesses just come flooding in, become consciously accessible and present themselves in the form of guilt, shame, horror and anger at the self.

The evidence that presents itself as the reality of someone's life choices and decisions unfold is quite stunningly precise and you just can't contradict it, no matter how hard you would otherwise try to cling to the illusion that "everything's alright, really ..."

This is both frightening as we've said before, but it is also a considerable time saver and brings such matters under control far more easily - a person does not have to spent another ten years in misery until the final breakthrough awareness descends upon them randomly, perhaps whilst waking up in a gutter yet again, with a hangover and no handy therapist to help out and encourage through the process when the blinding insight finally strikes.

This is the abreaction stage of the Guiding Stars protocol; please use the approaches described for this.

Dark Night

The next step stone in the process is what you might call a "dark night of the soul" experience - the insight has been made, the awareness has broken through into reality and the person is left with the ruins of their illusions and all their protective devices, shields and barriers in tatters.

This is not a pleasant place to be and this of course, is one of the main reasons why folk will do just about anything, including committing suicide, to avoid to ever to have this happen to them.

However, once there, there is absolutely no turning back.

A real change has occurred already, a shift that cannot be undone. The illusions are broken and can't be fixed. It is naturally at this stage to try to do just that, wander amongst the shards of the pottery and think with desperation if some glue could be found and enough effort expended to make the vases whole again - it is a fleeting thought because simply, it can't be done and the persons knows it full well.

The Guiding Stars pattern triggers this entire set of energetic events to take place rapidly and once the process is under way, it can't be stopped or reversed.

This is the reason for the all the very serious "health warnings" on this protocol. Very vulnerable, mentally ill or unstable people should not be taken through this - think of it as a major operation, if you will. Make sure your patients (and including your self) are of good enough health to withstand it before you start and do what pre-work is required before you start with this type of intervention. If it is a question of life or death, you will have to make a decision as to whether you want to risk it - but that's your choice and your responsibility.

What is required at this time is a stabilising influence only. The emotions and feelings here can't be taken away and I even have a notion that to attempt this might be counterproductive to the process as a whole. However, we can move through this level quite swiftly but it does require another to help accomplish this in safety who will support the process and be there in all ways.

Acceptance

Once the major storm has passed, we are in "acceptance" country. This is not a pleasant place either as the survivor climbs from the ruins and looks at the devastation of what there was before.

Energetically speaking, it is a far more calm and balanced state of being than the "dark night" and if you leave someone there, what will happen is that they will go out with some extra knowledge and insight but a pervading sadness and depression that is born out of profound loss and hopelessness, which is exactly the same energetic state as you would find with bereavement.

To get out of this state, use the opening statements of sorrow and loss which naturally arise. This clears the way for the next step and now what is needed is a form of review of what has happened.

This represents the first step for the complete re-organisation of many different components in the neurology and in the energy system.

Review

I mentioned before that you really need to talk about your insights and what has happened to someone else to get things straight in your own head at this time. A major upheaval has occurred and this is a crucial part of the essential sorting process which precedes the next steps in action in a most necessary and structurally important way.

Now, once again, this review does not need to take days, weeks, years in psychoanalysis.

On the contrary. As the patterns have emerged as to how and why are very high level and global, they are often very, very simple indeed - remember the "Ice cream in my mouth = experiencing love" and the "I know when I'm loved when I sit on the lap of a man who smells of alcohol." connections.

It's simple enough but it needs to be reviewed as the client (or your self) flashes through the connected memories, has the insights, and recognises their own patterns over time.

It is in the Review state that the real feelings of horror, shame and guilt at one's own part in proceedings and how they affected not just our own lives, but that of others, become strongly apparent, like a groundswell in the background or a distant thunder.

If you stop there, you will leave the client (or yourself) in a seemingly reasonable state but it is a very dangerous state to be and to remain there for any length of time will cause enormous expenditures of energy as well as a rising sense of terror at what will happen when the wave strikes for real.

It is most helpful to tap throughout the review state as this will pave the way for more flow in the client's energy system which of course, is of the essence for the moment when the final understandings click into place and the client sees for the very first time the entire picture of what has happened and how it came to be.

Riding The Wave

Guiding Stars sessions being what they are, there is actually not a lot either you or the client can do to avoid the arrival of the wave. It happens quite automatically and naturally, and it is made out of a huge mixture of emotions - shame and guilt of course, anger, disappointment, pure horror, a true, "Oh dear God, what have I done?" experience.

Once again, and with the wisdom of hindsight, it is a natural process that is quite necessary to move along the path of unfoldment and healing; there is nothing inherently bad about it and it need not take much time at all - perhaps a few moments, a few minutes, but that's it.

Think "flow" the whole time you are with your client in this pattern.

It moves the whole time and to flow with it makes it far less threatening and frightening than to tense up and resist the process - this will only drag it out and make it far, far more painful than it was ever designed or intended to be.

What moves the client (and yourself) out of this stage and into the next is simply to answer that question of , "My God, what have I done?"

Here again, all the energy interventions you know to repair broken channels, heal contortions and remove old blockages will prepare the client for the next step.

The technical term for the act of answering this question with truth and honesty is the ...

Confession

I have often thought that I was far more of a confessor than a therapist.

Confession is a most profound energetic intervention in its own right, much, much more powerful than most people will ever know.

Creating the space for confession and helping a client to find the strength within them to really face their problems and then to speak the truth aloud is incredible as a neuro-energetic process and very powerful indeed for both parties involved in this relationship event.

Anyone who has ever engaged in the act of a true confession will know that it is very similar indeed to an energy unblocking event – tension releases, a "huge weight is lifted off my heart", this is how people describe what that feels like.

Confession can only proceed when someone has come to the point of taking full responsibility for what they did and stop blaming anyone else, making any kind of excuse, rationalisation, "yes but", offer any kind of explanation for their actions but instead, just simply state how it is without any buts, becauses, ands or anything else tacked on to divert us from the central point of pain we have tried to keep from our awareness for so long.

It is literally the act of standing up and saying out loud, "My name is Peter and I am an alcoholic." There is something about this particular energetic movement and occurrence that is truly extraordinary - there is a decision there for change, for acceptance of things and self as to how they truly are, which indeed is the only place from which any further change can ever derive at all.

Those amongst us who have ever "confessed" in this way will know that it is not an easy thing to do, that it requires tremendous courage and the fear beforehand is tremendous as well.

However, if you have had the experience, you will also recognise and know the intense relief confession brings to you, the intense sense of having released a huge burden that was pressing all the joy out of you and what a relief it is.

For that feeling alone, it is worth it. Confession is so important because we have now really turned the corner - note that the emotions are changing from utter desperation into relief. The flow is turning the spiral loop into different kinds of energetic states - this is your indication that a true healing is taking place as the pain recedes, the system begins to relax and the energy becomes different, thus being differently interpreted as "positive", beneficial or desirable by most who would label human experiences in that way.

Of course, and how beautiful is this, we do not need to leave it there. We can now take the confession statement and treat it with EFT in order to achieve more, deeper, further healing on the topic and thus indeed, releasing the client from that which they confessed to once and for all.

This is important, because the next step is being able to receive something which cannot be done whilst one is still deeply involved with the issues which powered the confession.

Absolution

Now that is a heavy term indeed and indeed, it is little wonder that it has been confined to priests over the ages.

In simple procedural terms it is nothing more than to hear the confession and then to say or do something to have this be so AND YET IT IS ALRIGHT.

You probably know when we get right down to it, that we are all already forgiven totally and fully, in all ways, indeed, that the whole forgiveness thing was just a delusion of some kind in the first place - there is nothing at all to forgive.

No matter what, no matter how terrifying the acts and their repercussions, when you bring in true light and the love of the Universe, time and time again you find there is nothing to forgive at all at the end of the day.

I would say that absolution is the act of having someone understand this and that it is achieved in many different ways, depending on the circumstances and the individual involved.

For some, the fact that you heard the confession and you did not leave the room, run away screaming or jumped up and shouted, "Be gone, evil one!" is in and of itself an extraordinary and profoundly valuable absolution experience.

Some need you to say out loud that you forgive them, absolve them; some need to feel it from within themselves; some need to be guided to make contact with an idea, an entity or a part of themselves that will be the one to offer the absolution (this includes representations of the victims, angels, spirit guides and prophets, depending on the real views of the individual involved).

You know that the redemption process is complete when there is no anger, shame or guilt, excuses or rationalisations left at all and the client is calm and accepting of both their part in the unfolding events, as well as that of any other parties involved.

Here and again, we can smooth away the obstacles to absolution which is a feeling (and hence, a state of being) by removing resistances and blockages to receiving this powerful energetic clearance from "the sins of the past" and allow an individual to really have their prison sentence finally be over and to step into clear and bright new morning of the rest of their life.

Comments On The Redemption Patterns

As with the Guiding Stars pattern, this is not a pattern designed to "tap away" feelings of guilt and shame which are systemic and a natural part of the whole process.

Instead, the application of EFT is advised when the client (or yourself) are clearly stuck somewhere and can't move forward and complete the healing process that this pattern represents.

Think of this as a natural process very much like a physical injury sustained and the various pains and sensations that occur, all the way from the original shock of the injury, the acute pain, the throbbing pain and all the other sensation as the wound begins to close and heal.

When the process moves along without getting stuck or an infection occurring (and this is the metaphorical equivalent of meanings that will keep the wound from healing), it is remarkably swift and concluded successfully within a reasonable time span.

It is helpful to really explain to clients that it is a natural process, there are steps to healing, what to expect and to encourage them to let the system flow as it was designed to, in their own time.

Look for blocking meanings in this process - simply asking questions such as, "I can't admit to this because that would mean ...", "I can't ever be forgiven for this because that would mean ...", "I can't be absolved from this because that would mean ..."

Please use words that make sense to the client (or you) in the context; many people have negative reactions to religious sounding words such as forgiveness, redemption, confession and absolution so please replace these words with others, such as letting go, releasing, healing, being entirely free, being loved, and so forth.

The Redemption Pattern – Conclusion

The redemption pattern is NOT religious in nature; it is an energetic evolution that is natural to people and entirely systemic.

Not everyone can go through all the steps in this pattern swiftly; for some, time is needed to process each one of these shifts and find a new balance.

It is important to not push clients or the self towards "forgiveness" when they are not ready to do so; and indeed, you will notice that forgiveness isn't even a feature of this pattern at all. There are serious structural problems with the concept of forgiving, most notably the power threshold this implies as well as the presuppositions of wrong doing in many people's minds that cause severe problems when attempting to get to the absolution state, where all is cleared, all is healed and there is no danger at all of doing anything like that ever again.

Always remember that the **state of forgiveness** is something that naturally arises when the injuries sustained from the original incidents have finally healed. It is an effect, a measurement device to let us know how far we have come so far and not a standalone goal in and of itself.

The process of redemption itself is most likely very familiar to you already; you might not have put it in these words nor listed the stages as I have done in this chapter, but the structure of the unfolding events - energetic mind body states with their corresponding emotional charges from injury (sin) to healed (absolution) - is well known to most therapists.

It is in my opinion a crucial part of all release and personal development and healing endeavours and I would encourage you to pay attention to this process in all contexts, and not just Guiding Star type interventions but trauma healing, too.

Guiding Stars - In Conclusion

The Guiding Stars Pattern is very important for a number of different reasons.

Working with trauma alone has set the limit of what can be known about the formation of human concepts in a very real sense. As trauma is so negative in experience and manifestation, there are many aspects that could simply not emerge because naturally, we wish to alleviate suffering and avoid it too, whenever possible.

The underlying idea that led to the Guiding Stars pattern and protocol was that highly charged emotions are structurally the same, be they negative or positive, and that their effects on the neurology are also the same - the way these highly charged emotions are a guiding mechanism as to what to do, what to feel and think and how to behave.

In working with the Guiding Stars protocol, you will find out some very interesting things especially relating to beliefs formation that may also be applied to trauma memories.

Guiding Stars and trauma are of course, not the only kinds of experiences we have. Milder versions of "positively" and "negatively" charged experiences (I call these Diamonds and Coals, respectively, to keep a clear sense of the extra-ordinary nature of both Guiding Star AND true trauma experiences, which are of a higher order and structurally different) are also important devices that shape our internal worlds, and in so doing, shape our experience with the external world in turn.

I would offer this for your consideration and to try some of these approaches out in practise.

Do be careful with this pattern.

It is not for everyone and it is not one of those things you can safely do with anyone and just anywhere.

There are many therapies and approaches that are so wonderfully safe because they don't do anything much.

Guiding Stars is not one of these. It is a very powerful pattern and set of presuppositions.

Use it with discretion and with care.

Treatment Of Addictions With EFT

Addictions - what a vast and wonderful field this is.

Let me begin by stating that in this manual, we are using the word "Addiction" for any activity that is repeated and seems out of the control of an individual.

This is in essence the 12 Step definition but not necessarily the current psychological one. The trainers who decided on the content of the AMT MET Practitioner Training agreed that the wider definition of addiction is very useful in so far as the processes, roots, principles in action and underlying strategies to alleviate these types of problems are the same. It is useful to look at the addiction paradigm in that way because it makes sense of many seemingly bizarre behaviours that humans would engage in, willingly or otherwise.

In general, addictive **behaviours** replace or alleviate neurological processes that are perceived as intensely threatening by a given individual. Please note I use the phrase "perceived" which is of course, once more, one of our leverage points for change later on.

Addictive behaviours occur in response to a red alert in the neurology that something else needs to be done NOW or else something very, very bad will happen.

In the case of substances such as nicotine, cocaine, food, and so forth, the substance in question becomes mixed up in this and causes much confusion, so to begin with, we will look at addictive processes that do not entail external agents but are created within the client's neuro-physiology itself.

The Reasons & Use Of Repetitive Behaviours

It might not be high psychotherapy, but I think I can say quite happily here that the purposes of addictive behaviours is not to think about certain things, not to feel certain emotions, not to re-experience certain things that are so unbearable that the system believes it would lead to serious damage if these things were ever re-experienced.

This is a natural protective device that exists in all mammals, not just in people.

When the entire neurology is in a place where systemic damage is imminent, action is taken to protect the central systems and you get escape mechanisms clicking into place quite automatically, such as fainting, withdrawal, autism, coma, and at the lower end of the scale, repetitive behaviours designed to induce trance and keep the neurology safe in that state, in effect taking it out and away from external and other internal stimuli.

Head weaving in horses and elephants, for example, exist in primates and in humans too if they cannot escape in physicality and have no power to change the environmental conditions they find themselves in.

These obviously disturbed behaviours are the high end of a scale of less obvious behaviours resulting from the same process - everyone does addictions of one kind or the other, every day, as a matter of course.

Your Addictions

There is no way to learn about addictions from the inside as perfectly as to consider your own.

This does not only help you understand the processes involved on a most profoundly more useful level than just talking about it, but it will help with rapport with clients who present with high end addictions that are threatening their health and making their lives unbearable.

As a mental exercise to this end, I want you to consider what strategies you personally use in times of stress to find relief and release, take a "holiday in mind" from the problems of your environment and in effect, produce a state shift into energetic states where the problems that plague you in your ordinary states of being simply no longer exist.

I'd like you to consider three levels of threshold severity of this.

1. At the starting point, small addictive behaviours that go quite unnoticed unless you start to look. These may be mistaken for "habits" or "rituals" and there is of course, the possibility that these are one and the same, or become one or the other, over time.

2. Medium range addictions. These are clearly addictive behaviours and your nearest and dearest might have commented or more likely, complained about you doing these things under certain stressful circumstances.

3. High range addictions. This is behaviour that if it went, you are sure you would cease to exist also. Before you go and say, "Oh I don't have any of those", consider a Zen question I have always found useful in this context: "If you had to give up everything, what would scare you the most?"

* Please note - I am not asking you to tap these addictive behaviours away or to give them up, this is simply an exercise in recognition.

Addictions & Fear

It has been noted many times that at the root of all addictions lies fear.

I might make the comment that the severity of addiction, once again, is in direct correlation to the fear that is beneath it, or any of the other layered emotions you might find and treat in the course of your client's explorations.

Therefore, a non-stop, high end addiction that has pervaded 24 hours of every moment of a person's life will have serious emotions behind it.

When treating clients with high end, severe or long lasting addictions, please bear this in mind and remember the protocols we talked about when we spoke of abreactions and working with intense, very volatile material that might have been excluded from conscious awareness for decades in some cases, and with very good reason.

There is also merit in thoroughly reviewing the Energetic Relationships patterns in the context of addictions.

We will now go through the basic addictions protocol, a step at a time, and consider the special issues arising.

The General EFT Addictions Protocol

* Please note that this protocol is designed for more than one single session. It is meant to be usable for high end addictions and addictive behaviours including long standing substance addictions and also eating disorders and repetitive stress behaviours such as compulsive behaviours.

1. Rapport

Of course, we always endeavour to establish rapport with the client. That I mention this especially again here is because of the fact that you have to consider with addictions in particular that you are most likely talking to two clients, namely the one that wishes to change the status quo and the other one who fears this most intensely and doesn't believe or trust that it can be done safely or easily.

I have personal experience with addictions and time and time again in workshops and trainings, meet therapists who entirely fail to comprehend the depth, breadth and sheer intensity of the client's relationship with their addiction.

They may presume that the client of course wishes to be rid of this damaging behaviour/ substance AND behaviour when this is absolutely not so in most cases.

With some clients, even "going in" full steam against the addiction demon will shatter rapport on a profound level and cannot be re-built; it is the end of the treatment or any hope for successfully concluding it before it has even begun.

If you have no personal experience with high end addictions or have not thought about or endeavoured to change such addictions with the help of another, you must be especially careful and just take my word for it. Be very, very careful, and very, very respectful of the client and their own experiences. Please give the client room to express their doubts and fears and their resistances fully and without judgement, without trying to bulldoze them into feeling differently from what is actually the case.

The other deal with addiction clients is that you need to give them some time. I don't mean weeks or hours, but you have to have their agreement before proceeding. When I say agreement, I mean whole hearted, forward pointing "client avidity" (as opposed to client resistance or the unfortunately termed "client compliance", which is absolutely not enough with addictions).

Further, more than with any other type of problem any client would see you about, trust is of the essence. With some clients this takes longer to establish than with others but you must be prepared to give the time, not rush them, else they will rush out of your door just as fast as they have rushed out of all the other treatments, clinics, psychologist's offices they have rushed out of during their long battle with their problem.

This consideration leads us directly to the next step.

2. What Were The Previous Treatments Received?

There is much merit in having the client answer this question at as much length as they wish to answer it.

They will tell you many, many things about their beliefs, where the other treatments failed, and most importantly, about the main areas where your pre-work needs to be targeted to overcome this problem once and for all.

As the client speaks, make a note of the most important opening statements. Note down more rather than less; you can discuss later with your client in which order and sequence they would like to approach this.

This question will also give you indication of what you're up against by the way of long term resistance (read desperate protection from something much worse).

Take your time over this with addiction clients. It is essential to your success.

3. Current Treatment And State Of Affairs?

This will tell you if there are other treatments in action - methadone for heroin addicts, AA support groups, and a number of other important pieces for your jig saw puzzle that need to be taken into account before we start formulating opening statements.

It will also give you much insight of how much of the client's day to day life revolves around the addiction.

In this section, you will also enquire as to the details of the addiction and the behaviours it entails. I personally prefer to stay entirely calm and matter-of-fact as the client tells me how the addiction manifests in their lives, in their daily routines.

It is important you should let the client speak and tell you to a point where you are beginning to get a sense of what it is like to live like that.

Now, I am aware that many practise EFT like a technician and apply the methods like a mechanic would apply a drop of oil to a squeaky hinge. I personally don't think that's particularly useful, and least of all in the case of addictions where you might well have memories, strategies and all sorts of things hiding from both you and the client.

You need your intuition and your intuition needs to be with the client, be connected to the client and gather information in that way.

You also need a sense of where not to go just yet - more of this later.

4. Time Line Of The Problem

We now ask when and where it all began, how it developed and how it came to be as it is now. It is possible that the information gathered here will eventually lead to the specific topics, memories, beliefs, injuries received you will start working with when the treatment starts properly. At this point, we don't tap. We gather intelligence. Addictions are complicated systems - underestimate them at your peril only.

In the context of the genesis of the problem, please also be aware of the existence of pre-addiction behaviours that served the same purpose and were replaced by the current addiction. Cigarette smoking may have been preceded by thumb sucking or nail biting, heroin may have been preceded by other drugs, eating disorders can take over from other compulsions and so forth. When you are looking at such correlation chains from or towards the (suspected) genesis point/s, make a mental note of treating the pre-behaviours before treating the main addiction. In the odd case or two, it entirely collapses the problem and in many more cases, makes it far, far easier to deal with the main presenting problem.

182

5. Anti-Anxiety Protocols

Now we begin to diverge from the standard types of MET protocols by introducing immediately and before we go into any treatments the Anxiety Protocols. Addictions are about fear, about terror, about fear of other deeper, darker emotions such as shame. Even thinking about thinking about thinking about giving up or stopping an addiction can produce such intense anxiety peaks that this is where it can all grind to a halt, there and then.

In the successful treatment of high end addictions, it is essential to develop a personal short cut sequence with the client is particularly useful in all anxiety related problems. The classic EFT protocol is too long in a moment of true need. A short sequence of no more than three points or a single emergency stop point is needed. It is important that this sequence is short, well practised and that the client remembers it even under stress and in a state of panic, else it is useless.

6. Addictions Pre-Work

In most, but not all cases of addictions, it is essential to do some pre-work on certain issues to prepare the path for a smooth central intervention that is not resisted and fought against by parts of the client.

Ask any client the following questions. If they answer congruently with strong belief that they have no objections and no problems with any of these, you've spend five minutes doing very tidy work. But in many cases, you will find Guardians here, beliefs, rationalisations, fears and in general, "disturbances" of all kinds that hold lock and key on the real issues.

Here are some example questions for pre-work with addictions:

- What feelings do you have about having this addiction?
- Do you have any doubts as to the possibility of this being successful?
- Do you have any conflicts about releasing this addiction?
- Do you have any fears regarding any part of the process?
- Do you believe you can do this?

- Is there anything missing that you might need to succeed with this?

- What would happen if you were entirely without the addiction? What do you think?

This is, of course, a safe and ecological way to now start the treatment.

You can have the client tap on anything you have discovered about them and their relationship with the addiction. This will give you an indication of how responsive to the MET treatment they are, what they need from you in the way of encouragement or further explanations and indeed, during this pre-work you are getting to find out how to work together as a team to undo the client's blockages and disturbances in a fairly safe environment and without bringing the addiction itself into the arena.

I ask the client once in a while if they are ready yet to begin treating the addiction itself. Being unsure in and of itself is in my books a clear sign that there is much fear there that needs to be addressed properly before we go into the treatment.

Addiction & Ecology

Addiction ecology is a very interesting topic. Addictive behaviours, especially the kind that have someone seek help (do bear in mind that addicts will do just about anything rather than facing the problem or getting to that point where someone will stand up in front of a stranger and say, "I am Peter and I am an alcoholic."), have a habit of really running people's lives in a profound way.

With such involvement with just about everything they do, ecology becomes difficult. What will they do when they don't do the addiction anymore, and all the actions around the addiction that make it possible in the first place? I am talking about very practical things here - heroin addicts, for example, who don't have a good job really spend most of their time planning where the money for the next dose is coming from. Computer addicts construct journey routes and their entire schedule that they are never further than five minutes from a telephone line. You take that out, and what is left for them to do?

The neurology abhors a vacuum and many behaviours related to the addiction have really now become ingrained habits, absolutely enmeshed with and often, important parts of a client's life. Then there are our usual concerns with Primary and Secondary Gain, as well.

In practise, once an addiction has successfully resolved with MET treatments, the ecology seems to take care of itself - the person thinks new thoughts and new behaviours replace the old quite automatically.

However, when you first start out and with clients who are unused to how METs work, thinking this is some form of psychotherapy, they don't know that yet and cannot imagine a life beyond the addiction.

There comes a point in the treatment of an "addict" where they begin to wake up to the very real possibility that the "addiction may be removed" and they have to leave your office without it. That's a moment of intense panic, and the reason I am mentioning the "What is left for me to do?" question at some length is because it is a crucial time.

It is a supremely important question that goes to taking the ego or identity of the client from the now state into an unknown future state - this is one of the biggest fears, that I will never be the same again. A kind of death, if you will.

Allow the client to express these fears of the future without the addiction fully and completely and do not under any circumstances try to chivvy them up or tell them everything will be alright. Rather, have them tap on these fears and note with interest how the future that wasn't there before at all, begins to unfold for the client all by themselves.

There is no other therapy on Earth that can create this and I would suggest you make a note of this process, for it is by no means limited to addiction clients, although here it is so clearly marked out for everyone to notice.

The Central Treatment Phase

I know that MET treatments are supposed to be fast and furious, but with addictions, please and for the love of God, take it slowly.

Don't get into the central treatment phase until you and the client are fully ready for this and the pre-work has been done satisfactorily.

Ask the client. I know I've said this before but it is so important. So very important. Ask them and then listen to their answers. Don't push them and don't hurry them. It simply doesn't work.

Now, and only when the client is ready to do so, we are starting on the central treatment process and will address the addiction and its genesis, outcomes, symptoms and relationship with the client directly.

The Genesis Of An Addiction

Something that is little known but has every bearing in the World on addictions is the fact that not just significant negative emotional experiences (trauma) produces long lasting behavioural and structural change in a person's mind and body.

We may presume that pain (that's another word for the symptom of an unhealed energetic injury, which I prefer) is there somewhere, but the whole deal with addictions is that they relieve the pain.

Imagine you had a raging toothache. You have suffered from it until you can't even think or feel anymore and you have become one with the pain. Someone gives you a packet of painkillers. You take one and the pain recedes.

There you sit, with the packet in your hand and you look at it.

Do you have a relationship with that substance, no matter how damaging doctor people tell you it may be?

You bet you do.

Now here's the deal.

Even with the toothache removed, the tooth removed even, the memory of what the packet of painkillers did for you remains.

Much as your thoughts, decisions, memories and feelings related to that event, that wonderful moment when the painkillers came to you and took your pain away.

So:

The Genesis of any addiction is **relief from pain**, and not the pain itself.

The pain, in a way, and what caused and still causes this, is a different issue as the relationship with the addiction takes on a life of its own, a system of its own, has been born, if you will.

Yes, a child comes from a parent but it also has its own life and even if you take the parent away, the child remains.

This is the puzzle and problem of addictions and why they prove to be so resistant to ordinary treatments and ways of trying to cure them.

If you don't do something about the original energetic injury that, if still not healed, will simply continue to produce more children, we're not helping the client.

But that is not enough.

We also need to consider the addiction itself as an entirely and fully fledged self sustaining system.

Addictive Relationships

Earlier in this chapter, I have used the phrase, The Addiction Demon. It is like that. It really has a life of its own and the client has absolutely a love-hate relationship with this demon of theirs who came to their rescue when they needed them most but who extracts the price for their services - ill health, relationship failures, different and other pain.

I do not believe it is possible to really cure addictions without addressing the client's relationship with the addiction, with the substance, with this presence in their lives that is both their protector and their slave master, both their saviour and their destroyer.

Positive intense emotions tie a person just as truly to any energetic occurrence as negative ones do and the most complex and intense relationships there are, are those where both are in action, sequentially, simultaneously, and a mixture thereof.

Protecting The Demon

There comes a point when, threatened with the forthcoming exorcism, the client might well turn and protect the demon from you and your interventions. After all, they have been true and always there for them when they needed them, for many years, and you're just some guy for hire for a few dollars an hour. I'd know where to place my loyalty under such circumstances!

There may be some merit to seek a form of re-integration with the system that was born out of pain and the necessity to alleviate this pain, with no help from God or any man forthcoming.

The client might need to hear actual assurances from you that you will not disrespect or disregard in any way what the addiction represents for this person, and how it has kept them from much worse harm and from death, in many cases.

You may even have to deal with real, true and profound bereavement issues in this context. It might sound strange to someone who has not experienced a deep addiction but trust me, it's true. With such clients, I would recommend you think of the addiction as though it really was a live person, a guardian angel that is absolutely real, and deal with it as you would with any being that deserves absolute respect and love.

Our third intervention point after genesis and relationship is that of the current symptoms.

Under this heading of course falls the cravings for the object of the addiction.

The Object Of Addiction

Our Demon tends to manifest in some proxy shape or form, or in a global gestalt that covers a number of proxy shapes and forms (as would be the case for a betting addict and their relationship with a roulette wheel, the casino, and so forth). Finding the Objects Of Addiction in some cases is the core breakthrough moment for MET treatments - they may be unconscious or never before addressed, no matter how much therapy that person might have had. This is particularly so in the case of the severe eating disorders such as anorexia and bulimia.

Tapping on the emotional connection strands to the Object of Addiction is very helpful to release the client from these particular emotional entanglements.

Addictive Cravings

I truly dislike the word, "cravings". It sounds miserable, and really doesn't do what goes on when an action or substance is required, needed absolutely and enough to override any form of will power or other strongly held beliefs and convictions, any justice at all, no more than "anxiety" does justice to the sense of ultimate terror involved in a true panic attack.

Tapping on and in the presence of needing the object of the addiction is one of the most profoundly useful EFT interventions ever as the need that is a pain, growing to unbearable proportions with every heartbeat the client holds against it gently recedes, is reduced, or removed altogether.

Handling The Turning Point

Here we are, once more, in bereavement country. Many beginner therapists overlook the fact that many clients are entirely horrified when something they desired so much for so long so very deeply just becomes a lifeless, uninteresting lump of nothing before their very eyes.

It is a very freaky thing and it can cause severe problems with and for the client if this isn't honoured properly, laughed off or brushed away as though it was nothing.

It isn't nothing. It is a turning point in a person's neurology and it brings a flood of questions in its wake that can cause a lot of trouble in the weeks, months and years that follow, along the lines of, "If this can be undone so easily, what does that mean about me? About the years I have spent enslaved to this? Am I such a fool? Is there nothing I can feel that is real, that has any meaning at all?"

How exactly you handle such a moment with a client must depend on everything that went before, but be very careful and very reverend. Get this bit wrong and your client might have stopped smoking but will kill themselves 6 months later by jumping off a bridge - and I'm not joking, either.

Positive AND Negative Emotions

When you're tapping on Objects of Addiction or substances, you must remember to tap on both the positive emotional entanglements as well as the negative ones to get truly clear of the OOA or substance respectively. Forget one or the other, and you'll leave the famous hook - relationship strands that become stronger again over time and from which the entire problem may regrow.

An Experience - Loving The Strawberry

Find a piece of food or suchlike substance that you like and perhaps even "crave" sometimes, but you "know it ain't good for me" and you struggle against a closer relationship with it, such as consuming the relationship, as it were :-)

If your struggles take place in a supermarket and you don't have this in the home just in case you develop a craving for it, go out and acquire an example item.

Place this item in your kitchen on the worktop.

Place your elbows on the worktop and look closely at the OOA.

Now allow yourself to freely consider what you feel about this entity, what you think about it, what your conflicts about it are, what you believe about it.

For now, just take your time and allow yourself without any reservations or censorship to think what you think. All of it.

Then, make a note of what you remember about what you felt and thought.

You may, after completion of the notes, consume the item.

190

Releasing The Strawberry

Now it is time to face the OOA again.

This time, and with your note pad by your side, tap yourself for everything that's on the pad. Between each round or algorithm, break state by walking around and drinking some water before returning for the next one.

Make a note on what happened with each of the opening statements/set ups/topics on your pad.

Physiological Addictions

One of the great pre-fears of addicts in considering "giving up" especially real substances that are said to be highly addictive and cause extreme withdrawal symptoms and terrible pain, is of course the fear of the "drying out process".

Some may have had experiences of such processes without the aid of EFT and without any way to really relieve the terror and total panic that makes every single true physical symptom a hundred times worse from the inside of the experience and may be totally traumatised by such withdrawal attempts.

Thereby, and obviously, you will need to seriously address the traumas of previous treatments (I've had clients who have been treated with ECT for addictions, have been handcuffed to a radiator for four days by a loving relative and that's just the tip of the iceberg) and experiences of withdrawals, as well as the beliefs about how that is, how it is supposed to be and how it will be again.

Withdrawal traumas are not widely recognised as real "hooks" and stoppers for addicts to make the change and get away from their personal demons. I would put to anyone who may laugh at this type of thing and cite it as yet another example of the character flaws of junkies that I'd like to see them even trying to think of doing something again that the last time had them feel they were being boiled in oil for eternity.

For many therapists who have never experienced the reality of a true addiction themselves, rapport with addicts is difficult if not impossible. I would make the point that "beliefs about addicts", what they are like, what their character flaws might be and how much you like them has everything to do with the success of the treatment. In the face of the demon lip service won't do. You need to be congruent and have at the very least, a deep and profound belief that no matter what went on before with this one client, it **is possible to overcome addictions, release them totally and be absolutely free of them**.

The truth is that the therapist/counsellor/healers attitude towards addiction clients is more important than three hundred excellent protocols.

Homework In Addictions Treatments

Of course, nowhere is homework as centrally important as with addictions.

And nowhere is it more important to make sure that you discuss fully with the client when and where they most expect they will need the help and support EFT can give them.

Please now review the Homework Protocol we discussed in the Treatment Flow section, especially future pacing. This will be make or break for your addiction clients.

In designing homework protocols for an addict it is essential to elicit their "dark moments" and the times and circumstances when the problem is the most acute and where possibly previous attempts at overcoming the behaviour have seriously run into the rocks and capsized them there and then.

Each and every homework protocol must be custom crafted for this one person and their particular problem sets **in the context of their lives and their environments**. More so than for any other type of problem, it is essential to really take the time to work with fears and doubts regarding the question as to whether someone will indeed be able to use EFT in whatever form in a moment of crisis and succeed with their goals for the treatment.

Linking up particular sights, sounds, smells and emotional states too as a trigger to **remember to use EFT** is an essential part of the homework protocol and as important as the homework protocol itself.

Supervision And Follow Up

I used to offer addiction clients blocks of sessions at a reduced rate, payable up front, and the amount of sessions I would suggest would be in keeping with the severity of the problem.

Right at the start, I would introduce them to the idea that we want to make not a radical change overnight, but a gentle unweaving that would be a great deal more satisfying than they would expect, not having encountered EFT before.

I am a great believer in follow up with clients, and most especially with addiction clients. If someone doesn't come back after three sessions and the next thing you hear, they've been found drunk in a gutter, something important was overlooked or life threw such stress at the person that the young change didn't have a chance to override.

Having block sessions already paid for gave me in many cases the reason and excuse to phone the person and have them continue in spite of major setbacks. Whether you choose to do this or not is of course entirely up to you, but I personally like to find out what happened in every case, regardless of whether the treatment was "successful" or not - there is always something to be learned, and even more so now, as we are truly dealing with brand new forms of interventions and therapy and really don't know yet what the long term effects and repercussions might be.

Something you might also like to consider as an option is to use the coaching model for longer term support with clients you have come to know quite well. A weekly or bi-weekly chat on the telephone for half an hour is affordable and doable; this kind of longer term motivational support can make all the difference to addiction clients.

Now, to sum up in brief, here is once more and in its entirety, the Addictions Protocol.

Please note this is in addition to the general treatment flow and does not replace this.

The Addictions Protocol In Brief

- **Treatment Received?**
- **Current Treatment?**
- **Time Line Of Problem**
- **Teach Anxiety Protocols**
- **Pre-Work**
- **Central Work**
- **Genesis of Disturbance**
- **Genesis of Addiction**
- **Relationship with Addiction**
- **Relationship with OOA**
- **Addictive Cravings**
- **Addictions Prescriptions**
- **Homework**
- **Supervision**

EFT As A Ritual - Emergency Situations, Emergency Measures

I had an interesting experience the other day.

I found myself in a situation which caused my emotional responses to "go off the Richter scale" - I was extremely disturbed by an incident, so much so that I was physically shaking and in shock.

I don't particularly think that I was thinking at the time, just got away from the situation as best I could and then, I started to tap.

EFT.

Not intuitive shortcuts, not personalised algorithms. Not choices or gauges or becoming one with the problem. Not any of the refinements or variations on the theme - EFT as a ritual.

Even though I don't understand this state I'm in, I deeply and profoundly love and accept myself. Three times repeated, sore spot. Start tapping the points, starting with the eyebrow.

Karate chop, then the gamut procedure. Count, sing, Count, do the eye movements.

Back to the eyebrow point and all the way through once more, take a deep breath.

I was still shaking but calm enough to start observing myself again, to note what I was doing and to have some conscious thought about it all and one of the very first thoughts I had was that I had engaged in the EFT "ritual" without a thought, when I was quite incapable of thought, automatically.

And how useful that was, how profoundly useful indeed.

This was a true emergency procedure, being performed "without me doing it", and without having to think about it. Something you can just do and it takes over because it is entrained, deeply learned, done so many times before that it can be done automatically.

The basic EFT procedure had on many previous occasions served to take me out of a state of deep stress at various levels and towards a calmer, more composed place - there is a precedence, a FLOW into the direction away from disturbance and towards clarity and calm.

This flow unfolds as the ritualised actions run their course; and as they run their course, predictably from one thing to the other, one behaviour to the next, one tapping point to the next, this structure in and of itself provides a steadying influence and a lifeline when all seems to be chaotic, when all seems to be out of control, when one has become overwhelmed with it all.

Rituals are used by humans in many different ways to this very end.

They do not just occur in a religious setting where the word might first make connotations; ways of getting from a state of ordinary awareness into a state of enhanced receptivity swiftly and smoothly, such as in ceremonies and meditations.

Rituals and ritual behaviours are used in many other ways, in many other places. Drilling soldiers step by step in their every movement is such a device, designed to create a state of mind that will allow someone to perform the requisite actions under the most exacting of circumstances. People use "home made" rituals of all kinds to keep themselves functioning when otherwise, they would not - from compulsive hand washing to sitting behind a computer screen for hours on end or staring at a fruit machine and a thousand more little rituals all across the day.

Some people dislike ritualistic procedures and training methods on the grounds that they would impede free will, turn someone into an automaton, but in the case of severe emotional disturbance, that's where we are already and that, indeed, is a good time for automatically - like an automaton! - engaging in a course of action that will restore Even Flow to the systems, that will take one out of the chaos and into calmer waters by the very act of performing the ritual.

I discussed this with a fellow therapist and she put forth the suggestion that the first kind of therapy one might have learned would be the one that would be chosen as "the ritual" in a crisis situation, but I disagreed with this assertion after some thought.

A great many therapies don't have any rituals for emergency situations at all - indeed, the majority of all psychotherapies don't. Therapy begins AFTER the event, in many cases a long time after the event, not in the middle of it or that close to it as I was on that particular occasion.

Also, and this important about rituals, is that many if not most therapies outside the field of MET do NOT have a kinaesthetic component to them - there is no ACTION, only talk and cognition.

In emergencies and under high stress, there is ACTION in the body - the heart beats high, in my case, I was trembling all over and exhibiting all the classic fight or flight responses. People in this state of distress often don't appear to hear it when another speaks to them or screams at them; they don't see someone waving their arms around in front of their eyes; and what tends to get through to them is touch - holding them, rocking them, physically restraining them.

Rituals do have action - always. It is what makes them work, how they lead into a more aligned mind/body state, through an alignment of thought and physical action. Sometimes, the physical action leads the way in this alignment (NLP calls "physiology the royal road into state" for this reason) and sometimes, thought precedes the first action, gives the command for it all to start; either way, when action and thought become aligned, the chaos recedes and a different state of mind comes into being.

You could call this a trance state, and indeed, it is.

For a mind and body in utter turmoil, the trance state is a resting place to regenerate resources and a step stone to start an emergence towards normal functioning.

Now, with general and unbeknown ritualistic behaviours, this is not always the case and the trance state that is acquired thus becomes the end result of the behaviour; if one was to look at the basic EFT protocol from this standpoint, it offers the added dimension of actually beginning to heal and rebalance in the very act of engaging in the ritual, so that an emergence is virtually presupposed, virtually guaranteed.

When I was having my crisis, that which distressed me so was still right before my eyes - I was still seeing the scene. When I began the automatic EFT routine, I was speaking the statements and hearing them, I was touching myself and feeling myself being touched; and as I went through the ritual that is the basic EFT protocol, I could feel myself calming and regaining some sense of self, of clarity, of thought even after the very first round with a probably not very well thought out opening statement.

The classic EFT routine is just long enough to give time for this to happen, for the ritual to unfold. A three point algorithm without speaking isn't the quite the same thing, nor is a oft repeated prayer that has no physical action associated with it.

This is why I would say that as a ritual for real emergency situations, the classic EFT protocol is probably the best practical thing I've seen so far.

I have included this chapter because I'd like to draw your attention to the concept of rituals and ritualised behaviours to help someone overcome these moments of chaos and derangement in a pro-active way; whatever therapy you practise by preference, there may be merit in considering what form of such a ritual may be created for your particular modality to deal with this very real circumstance, very real situation in which not only our disturbed clients find themselves repeatedly, but which can happen to any human, at any time.

We no longer say Hail Mary's or count rosary beads; something to replace these very useful behavioural mechanisms to use in a moment of overwhelm would be indicated.

I was also made aware of the distinction between working intuitively with clients in a calm place long AFTER the fact and being right in that situation that, generally, might have led me to see a therapist a few years later and after the symptoms and repercussions of the events had been such that I wouldn't have been able to go on without seeking help of some kind.

I'm really glad that I practised the basic EFT routine as relentlessly as I did.

I've been glad of this many times over the past few years for one reason or the other; there is a great deal to the classic EFT pattern, as it stands, simple as it might seem which reveals itself really only when one has spent considerable time with it and tested and experimented with it under many different circumstances, with many different people, and on the self, in many different states.

For a couple of years, I refused to learn any other form of MET and also did not seek to change or personalise the classic EFT protocol to make something else out of it that I might call my own. I sometimes wondered why I didn't, and I now wonder whether my experience the other night would be the answer to that question.

It might not be EFT that would be worthwhile practising just an army drill for emergencies - it can be your own therapy, your own shortcut, your own thing altogether.

But from my experience, I would suggest you make sure to have all the components there that made the "EFT Ritual" so very useful to me that night, namely:

- A ritualised procedure that takes at least five minutes to complete;

- which engages touch, feeling, seeing if possible, hearing and speaking;

- which has an emergence or test point built in (the deep breath at the end of an EFT sandwich);

- which follows a logical sequence of events that is easily remembered;

- and finally, which includes the rebalancing energy aspects of the MET treatments in general.

Practise this until it becomes second nature to your body and mind, entirely engrained, entirely remembered in all ways.

When the day comes, as it may or may not, when you really need this, it will be there for you - if you take the time now to install this safety anchor for yourself.

The EFT Body Protocol

Here is an extremely useful physiologically based protocol which I have backwardly engineered from EmoTrance™ to become a full EFT protocol so it can be used by anyone who is familiar with Emotional Freedom Techniques by Gary Craig.

To a considerable degree, the success and virtuosity in applying EFT to its full potential is to be able to formulate the correct opening statement, or should I say an opening statement that is close enough to direct the re-balancing effects of the EFT treatment in the right direction.

This has the disadvantage that unless there is a conscious conception of the problem, it can't be presented for treatment at all (see Shadow Emotions); this also represents a limitation when dealing with "body memories", i.e. experiences that are either not retained in consciousness at all (but are remembered or imprinted directly in the physiology) and also, in the case of the so called "repressed experiences".

With some problem, the disturbances in the energy system are an interlinked "problem group" and when this problem group contains body memories and/or repressed experiences, it cannot be successfully resolved - at the conscious level of investigation, it fully appears that there are no more aspects left, yet the problem still persists. One could think of this as being able to treat the available material like a part of an island showing above the water level, yet there being other parts to the island which are below the water level and therefore, out of conscious reach.

The EmoTrance system relies on working with direct, physiological experiences the client has to firstly, locate the disturbance in the energy system, and then to treat this disturbance directly, rather than via an abstraction, such as would be in the case in the description of an emotion, a feeling, a subject matter, a word, a memory etc.

As such, it has the following immediate benefits:

1. As there are no interface devices such as metaphors, words, emotional labels etc being used, it is impossible for the client to go into their ordinary thought processes about the nature and cause-and-effect of the problem. In the case of people who have either studied or engaged in a lot of therapy or counselling, this is a real blessing because there tend to

be prejudices and expectations of how things might have come into being - and these are often quite erroneous.

By not "talking about" the problem, much time is saved and many misleading directions need never be explored.

2. As a direct physiological response - a sensation rather than an emotion - is the directional device, it is comparatively easy to know when a problem has gone. The pain and the discomfort are gone and that is simply put, the greater convincer, even before the behavioural and cognition changes have been noticed.

3. It is virtually impossible for the practitioner to make any mistakes, because no further detective skills are required than to simply ask the client where in their body they experience the problem, and as the treatment progresses, to keep asking for feedback which directly guides the treatment sessions in the right directions.

4. The order and sequence of any aspects is taken care of as the most immediate and strongest physiological sensations are being treated, one after the other, as they present themselves.

5. As what is being treated are nothing more than disturbances in the energy system, the question of ecology doesn't arise or becomes non-sensical.

Clearly, there can be no merit in a weeping sore in the energy body, any more than there be any reason to wanting to retain such an injury in the physical body. The intervention is not so much one of change, but of simple healing and returning what was broken, to its rightful state of health and functioning.

All of the above core benefits can also be had with using EFT; this is possible by using the physiology directly and deliberately as the guide and entrance point to deciding what opening statements to use.

As this is both highly effective and extremely useful, I am very happy to be able to add to the Emotional Freedom Techniques repertoire with this Body Protocol and I am delighted to share it.

Tracking Disturbances Via The Body

Whenever there is a severe disturbance in the energy system, although people will notice what they call "emotions" by preference, this disturbance **always** has a physiological component, an actual physical sensation associated with the disturbance.

For example, when someone unexpectedly gets told, "You're fired!", they might report "feeling as though someone punched me in the stomach".

That sensation in the stomach is not psychosomatic but absolutely real and represents an indication of the underlying disturbance in the energy body.

Similarly, all and any so called emotionally based problems have one or more physical symptoms, sensations and locations.

These are found by asking the client, and the description becomes the EFT opening statement.

So, the person who was fired and still feels "emotional" about this event, will be asked,

"When you think about this problem, where do you feel it in your body?"

"It is in my stomach."

"And what does it feel like?"

"It feels like my stomach is sinking."

Which gives us the opening statement of:

"Even though my stomach is sinking, I deeply and profoundly love and accept myself."

The test is simply to ask the client to think of the scenario that had caused the disturbance again to find any other body sensations that would be treated in the same way.

Here is another example.

One gentleman had a very severe fear of public speaking he was sure had derived from being afraid of his father. Much psychotherapy and energy therapy had not resolved this, however.

When asked to think about getting up to speak in public, the following physiological sensations arose in this sequence:

1. His hands would go cold. ("Even though my hands are going cold, ...")

2. He became aware of a "huge pressure in his throat". ("Even though I have this huge pressure in my throat.")

There were the following other physiological symptoms in the original discussion but these did not occur again **after the throat treatment round** had taken place:

3. A trembling in the upper arms, shoulders and neck;

4. Dry mouth, swallowing rapidly;

5. Break out into sweat, hands first, then under arm, then head.

It is often the case that following a treatment for a sensation, such as the cold hands, the client derives all manner of new insights and connections that they had previously been entirely unaware of, no matter how much time they had spend in other therapies.

Here is one last example.

This gentleman suffered from "low self esteem" and "depression". When asked where he felt this problem in his body, he indicated his jaw with his hand whilst still consciously thinking about it for quite some time, then finally he said, "In and around my mouth, like a hard tightness."

This was treated straight up with no further discussion as to his history, past or any other treatments he might have had and within seconds of the energy disturbance having been resolved, he began to shout out loud, "I know what it is! How can anyone take me seriously if I never speak out for myself, never tell them who I am, and that I'm worth something!"

This is a good example how with these "sensation based" treatments often incredibly obvious connections come to light. However, they are only "incredibly obvious" with the wisdom of hindsight, and one must wonder how many years it might have taken to find out the connection and resolve it, if ever.

The questions, "Where do you feel that in your body?" and "How does it feel?" can be applied to any presenting problem at all and are absolutely not restricted to physiological problems.

The EFT Body Protocol In Brief

1. Enquire about the problem.

2. Ask, "Where do you feel this in your body?"

3. To formulate a precise opening statement, ask, "What does it feel like?" (3-5 proceed differently in EmoTrance).

4. Use the client's exact words they used to describe the physiological sensation to formulate the opening statement.

5. Apply EFT.

6. Enquire about the problem once more.

7. Repeat 2-6 until there are no body sensations remaining when the client thinks about the original problem or reports a major change, breakthrough or requests a pause before going further.

This protocol can be usefully employed for long standing global problems of any kind, and also for sensations "in the moment" even if they don't make any sense or seem entirely unreasonable. It is particularly useful for topics that seemingly have too many "conscious aspects", reasons, gains, contortions and other explanations as to why they absolutely need to be kept. Focussing on, and dealing directly with, the physiological sensation side-steps conscious based objections to healing and is extremely effective. I would suggest for practitioners to try this protocol on any of their own current or long standing situations, problems, seemingly irresolvable conflicts in order to get an understanding of how it is different from the standard thought and memory based approaches; and to get an understanding of how basic physiological feedback, simple straightforward sensations in the body, can hold the simple answers to what might have seemed like impossibly complex problems.

Touch And Heal - Working With Mind Maps

Working with Mind Maps in EFT treatments is a subtle and very elegant application indeed with much scope to make shifts in complex, multi-ordinate problem systems.

Firstly, and although you can absolutely make mind maps as complicated as it is possible to imagine, the basic idea is very simple and requires no more than a single sheet of paper and a pencil.

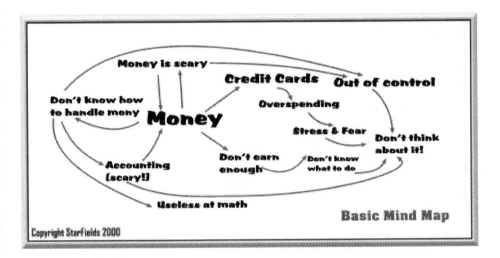

How To Make A Mind Map

1. Put the topic header of the problem erea on the paper – simply write down the word, whatever it may be. For example, "Mother", "Prosperity", "Self Esteem", "Health" or whatever it may be.

2. Now simply write down other topics as they come to mind, letting associations flow where they will. Draw lines between the topics and link them up in every way it feels appropriate to you.

3. When an association chain is finished, return to the central topic to discover more "aspects" and write these down too.

Now we have a basic mind map that shows a very simple representation of the main components of the problem group.

Next, we apply EFT as follows:

The Mind Map EFT Protocol

1. Touch a finger to the first topic that takes your attention when you look back to the mind map and with the other hand, start to tap. Keep looking at the topic and there is no need to say anything at all unless you really want to.

2. As you tap, you might find you want to stay entirely on the first word but you might also find that your attention shifts to a **different part** of the Mind Map. Follow your attention with your finger as you trace some connections, or touch other topic headings.

3. Continue to simply tap the EFT rounds (and not forgetting the Gamut and Karate Chop points) as your attention moves around the Mind Map and your finger follows your attention and "touches the topic".

4. If something new turns up, stop and put it into the Mind Map. Otherwise, simply continue until you feel you have had enough.

This is a truly interesting technique in many ways. Sometimes, new issues or topics become revealed or apparent which are even more important than the original central topic; you may need to make a second mind map for this new topic or you may be able to fit it onto the same sheet.

If you end up with more than one sheet of paper, it is a good idea to have them all side by side at one point and allow yourself to trace the connections.

Notes On The Mind Map EFT Protocol

- Something very important and interesting happens when you write the words and touch them at the energetic levels. There is a different kind of connection to the topic, much as though it was "brought out into the open" to be reachable and with the EFT protocol, finally treatable.

- Allowing your attention to wander across the map while you tap is a very elegant way of allowing your totality (unconscious mind, body mind, repressed parts of self etc.) a direct say in the so important "Order and Sequence" of unravelling the energetic contortions across the problem system.

- This protocol is particularly suitable for use with IEFT.

- I have presented this as a self help protocol but it is a really interesting client approach in many ways, and especially useful for clients that seem to have become stuck or seem to be going around and around their problem group with no exit in sight.

- Taking the Mind Maps (or a copy thereof) home after the treatment session for homework is often appreciated. The client can use it to treat themselves for aspects and topics and even more importantly, can add to the map as and when related new topics become revealed in between sessions.

- The Mind Map is of course a testing procedure in and of itself. You or a client can use it to track how their responses are changing and if topics have lost their emotional charge; and of course, extremely interesting changes can become revealed, as well as areas where more work is necessary by making a brand new map for the **same** topic as the first and comparing the two.

Healing Your World

A much more advanced and in-depth version of the simple "words on paper" map is to make what I call a World Map.

This involves giving over a considerable space to a problem group in your house – an entire wall of a room, for example.

Here, one can pin up for example:

- photographs,
- objects (jewellery, for example);
- original documents (birth certificates, marriage licenses, credit card statements, etc.);
- relevant works of art or drawings, writings, etc.

- post-it notes or longer or larger topic headings;

- collages;

... and in general, all and everything that an individual feels is important to bring the entire problem group out into the open.

Larger objects, such as possessions, belongings, gifts received etc. can be placed at least near the wall or elevated if this is important by standing them on a stool, for example.

The connections can be simply drawn on the wall (what is more important, re-painting a single wall in your house or resolving and healing a major problem group?) or by using low adhesive masking tape or string.

Just as with the paper protocol, all that needs to be done is to let one's attention be drawn where it wants to go and simply tap, tab or use IEFT to clear the emotions, entanglements and problems of this group whilst touching them and thus, being in a far more powerful connection than could otherwise be achieved.

This is a **very** powerful process and very personal indeed; you know it is complete when you can take all the objects away and return them to use or throw them out one by one, as soon as each relationship has been resolved in turn.

Any reluctance to take down or to change any part of this world map indicates that there are still areas and aspects left which sincerely wish to be understood, addressed and resolved.

Other Forms Of Map Healing

The concept of **externalising** the problem group to bring it out into the open so they may be healed need not be confined to the medium of classic mind maps.

Journaling

Some people keep regular diaries in which they confide deeply. These pages tingle with the energies expressed there, the conflicts between hopes and dreams and the problems and challenges the writer has experienced.

Of course, such journals as are all forms of creative writing and including letters, poems, songs are also a form of mind map.

Touching existing journals whilst treating oneself with EFT or IEFT can do much to resolve these conflicts at last and indeed, heal the past self who wrote those entries and who still exists now in the timeless quantum spaces of the oceans of energy.

Those who did not write journals or diaries can do so now and attain much the same effect by allowing themselves to remember what it was like "back then" and writing it down, thus bringing it out into the open very much in their own words which, as we know, are the keys to their own neurology.

If journaling sounds like too much of a task, a letter written by a past self or a short poem or description of the current problem group serves the same purposes.

If this technique is appealing to you or certain of your clients, beautiful and very profound shifts can be expected to occur.

Further Variations On Touch & Heal

There are literally innumerable variations of the basic idea of "touching something" to get in touch with the essence of it and what it represents in order to be able to heal it with EFT.

Clothes, locations on a map, objects and items, the pictures in a yearbook or a family photo album, the collar of a lost pet, a wall in a room of a house – as I said, the applications are limitless and indeed, include touching **people** who are currently in your life.

The EFT Fault Lines Protocol

The Body Speaks - Fault Lines & Early Warning Systems

I am sure you are familiar with how some chronic or recurrent forms of physical challenge or illness can drive Mind-Body-Spirit orientated folk to distraction as they try to figure out "the message".

For many this turns into quite a journey of personal development and exploration over time - only, the original symptoms never seem to abate or shift in the slightest, no matter what message may be assigned to it, and no matter how very real and useful the treatments turned out to be otherwise.

I have come to think of any form of recurrent and/or chronic physical problem more in the sense of this problem being a "fault line".

If you have a scratch in the surface of a sheet of glass, it will break there in preference and not anywhere else, regardless of where else you might apply the pressure. You could also think of this fault line occurrence as "the weakest link" or simply "the first to get it when the battle starts".

To get a sense of understanding this you might like to consider how and where you personally manifest stress of all kind (never mind how, who and what has caused it) in preference? Where is the first place where it will show? What are your physical symptoms - if any - that are resistant to treatment? If you have no physical symptoms, you may like to consider which psychological problems are manifesting in the forefront of stress - thoughts, beliefs, actions, addictions.

The fact is that for a sheet of glass to crack across the pre-existing fault lines, you have to put on a lot of pressure. One could say that if the glass was absolutely perfect, it could withstand more pressure and this is true.

However, if the pressure keeps getting turned up and in the absence of a fault line, a plate of glass will shatter chaotically into lots of fragmented splinters in a very unpredictable type of explosion.

If you cannot imagine this, try it for yourself with a piece of glass.

This is an important principle in healing anything at all and in conjunction with the lives we all lead.

There is a huge amount of pressure of one kind or the other by just simply living in any First World society. For sure, it is not the type of hunger/survival pressure our ancestors would have had to deal with but it is very real nonetheless.

There is environmental toxins pressure, there is faulty diet pressure, there is substance abuse pressure and then, there is an enormous array of psychological pressure of one kind or the other, much of it entirely ridiculous and entirely artificial such as the quest to be exactly like Superman and to never age at all which is rather new to humans and a recent innovation.

And again, and no matter how ridiculous it may seem, all of it is absolutely real because our neurology makes it so for us.

The "early warning sign" of migraines, skin problems, sleep disturbances, teeth grinding, nightmares and so on and on and on that are not in and of themselves a problem at all, but just the fault line showing that the pressure is beginning to go into the red. And these warning signs are removed only at some considerable peril.

If you take the gauge off because the red blinking light on the low oil warning in your car irritates you, something else will and must happen - not right away, but sooner or later with some serious inevitability.

Acute VS Chronic Problems

Acute means: One time incident following a particular experience (such as falling from a tree and now your leg hurts badly).

Chronic means: Symptom/s flare up again and again over time, seemingly unconnected to the original causative event and are extremely resistant to treatment (such as, your leg still hurts 30 years after your original fall from the tree, if there's too much stress or the weather changes).

There is merit in making a distinction between these two very different types of occurrences when you are trying to treat root causes or simply are attempting to alleviate the pain from the chronic problem to any degree because with one, you would be treating it directly, but the other can mislead as to its origin, genesis and alleviation.

214

Chronic Fault Lines & How To Treat Them

The symptom of a migraine may not have the message that it says in the standard "symptom = underlying belief" books on the market but instead, be a response to some other increase in pressure elsewhere.

Therefore, with chronic problems that have proven entirely resistant to treatments in the past, you are often best advised to leave them be altogether and talk about:

"What is causing you the most stress in your life, right now?"

... and treat that instead.

This will bring in its wake an immediately noticeable reduction in the fault line symptom as well as, of course, having considerable benefits on many other levels to the client.

The idea of Fault Lines is particularly interesting in another context as well.

As the Fault Line is what always demands attention and draws all attempts of healing and all thought to itself, it protects what you might want to call the "real problems" which are causing the most pressure on the system.

Indeed, it is my assumption that chronic Fault Line problems may indeed have been actually really healed many times before and simply re-occurred because with the increased pressure on the entire system (and the roots of which are as yet, entirely unknown and entirely out of sight) it became a Fault Line afresh, just as it did the very first time this strange and fascinating system came into being.

As strange as this may sound, with a true chronic problem the best solution might be to treat just about anything else but the problem itself and instead, to watch how the chronic problem responds "as a side effect" to the other treatments being performed, and other systems being released, unblocked and restored.

Please see also "Shadow Emotions" for suggestions of opening statements on this topic. Time line work and Mind Maps can also be interesting and useful to discover the real reasons for the constant pressure in the person's energy system which is causing the chronic Fault Line manifestations.

The EFT Healer Model

This protocol starts with the assumption that Proxy EFT can be used by the therapist/facilitator to **treat themselves** surreptitiously for perceived energy blockages in the client whilst they are in rapport with the client and thus in touch with the state of the client's energy system.

This requires either a degree of natural sensitivity to energy based work, or some experience with clients and the way their energies shift when EFT is applied, but both will become naturally more reliable and more strongly noticeable as your proficiency with the technique grows and contacting the client's energy field becomes part of your repertoire of unconscious competence.

With a little practise, this can be done conversationally and instantly.

The client may say something which indicates an underlying trauma (read blocked or disturbed energy flow), either by

- what they say (meta model violation) or
- how they say it (voice shifts, breathing disturbances, gestures, body postures, body and facial expressions, incongruencies).

You can comment on this or ask them to talk more about this topic, and whilst they speak, touch the points you have perceived as being relevant to the problem **on your own body**.

With sufficient rapport, this will produce a noticeable shift in the client which will then be reflected back to you in their physiology, new cognition on the problem and of course, their and your energy states.

For your interest, here is the progression of events that are taking place when learning to recognise the physical sensations relating to energy shifts, and how to learn to manipulate the energy system in a non-physical fashion.

I call this the "natural healer progression" or, for short, "The Healer Model".

7 Steps To Pure Energy Healing

1. The first step to be able to do all sorts of wonderful things with this system is to tap on yourself for various problems and focus on the problems and how you feel differently afterwards in order to familiarise yourself with your own kinaesthetic feedback devices for energy manipulations.

2. At some point you begin to notice as you tap that certain points feel different from others as you tap on them; this goes hand in hand with noticing and recognising your own physical signs for energy shifts, such as yawning, tearing of the eyes, a feeling of heat or coolness in some part of your body, stomach muscles relaxing - it's different in different people.

3. After a while, when you tune into a problem or emotion, you will be able to notice certain tapping points "lighting up" (giving you a kinaesthetic response) even before you tapped on them. This is problem specific - for one problem the one on the side of the eye begins to become noticeable, for another the index finger begins to tingle etc.

4. When this happens, you can try switching to just placing your attention on the points that have become noticeable; experiment what you have to do to make them feel normal again. Some people "stroke the point" with their attention, others imagine extra energy flowing into the point, others just focus on the point until it feels normal again. An Important Note: As you play with this, do make sure to get as good results with the intention only tapping as you did with the physical tapping. If you do not, you need to back up to the physical tapping and spend a little more time here - practise makes perfect! Remember it's the actual result that counts, not how you got there. There are no brownie points on offer for doing the advanced energy work badly!

5. When you can really "feel" the points during interventions for yourself, try getting into rapport with someone and feeling "their points" with your body. Tap the points thus discovered and reality-check if you've got it right. More practise, more rapport, deleting some limiting beliefs first or more focussed attention may be required to make it work.

6. The next step is to then manipulate another's points by attention as in No. 4.

7. When this process has become entirely unconscious and does no longer require your attention at all but is simply and automatically happening, you have reached the outcome state of this model.

If we take this progression to its logical conclusion, then we would have the following as outcome states with some practise:

The client only speaking about their problem and it being resolved by the healer **as they speak** and by the time they are done, their problems are healed also.

The client only **thinking** about their problems and by the time they are done, the problem has been healed.

Healer and client sitting quietly, neither speaking or thinking very much, and both emerge from the "treatment" entirely resolved, relaxed and restored.

Am I joking? No, not at all.

We have evidence at the lower scale of this "Healer Progression" that these kinds of processes are indeed, real, existing and in action in straightforward classic EFT treatments.

It stands to reason to follow the progression and if you did, that is exactly what you would get – two people in a room, healing each other without a word being spoken at all.

We are on the lower floors of a healing high rise, indeed ...

The EFT Inner Child Healing Spiral

Regardless of what your involvement may be in personal development, healing, learning etc., I would strongly encourage you to read this chapter carefully and read it to the end, and most importantly, not to pre-judge the contents for its terminology or in terms of modality.

This is actually a Sidereus Energy Healing pattern which I have translated across into the EFT modality to make it easy to use, easy to understand, and easy to do with self or with clients.

It is globally useful, stable and ecological and I would offer it to you with the hope that you will not only read it, but use it.

EFT & Inner Child Work

About a week ago, a young man by the name of Paul killed himself with a heroin overdose. He was 24 years old, very intelligent, very talented.

Following his death, someone said, "I feel so guilty about this. I knew him for five years and I feel responsible. I could have done more to help him."

I said, "Get in line. Have you seen Murder On The Orient Express? I was there too, and so were at least a dozen other people. But before he ever got there, what about all the other people involved during the time of his life? His mother who left him, the various foster homes, the children's homes, all the teachers and social workers involved who "processed" him in that time, the drug dealers, his friends, his relatives - well, as I said, get in line. It's a very, very long line, and at the end of the day, by the time we knew him the damage had been done. By the time he was six years old, it was near enough all over."

This set me to thinking.

About the fact that a single sentence placed to a young child can do and undo more than 30 years spent in therapy for an adult.

And about the fact that the parts of us that remember what it was like to "be that child" live still in quantum space, and, it being a **quantum space** that we can make changes now that will re-write history then.

The November Man & His Lessons

Milton Erickson, the famous hypnotherapist, once had a very special client. This was a man who had been kept by his lunatic religious fanatic parents in a dark cellar his entire life and was only found upon their death. He had no understanding of the world and no social skills of any kind. Over a period of time, Milton Erickson would age regress him and appear to him as the November Man, a person who would take him out of the cellar and have him experience a playground, a family dinner, a walk to the shops, a holiday by the sea, so that the man would have "childhood memories" that would become templates to base his current behaviour on.

There is much literature on "Inner Child" work, and for all of you who dismiss this idea as some kind of lame new age fascination, please read on. It is my supposition that this is the most important type of personal development and HEALING work you could ever undertake - if you have the courage.

I am going to suggest some approaches to begin your own IC Healing explorations, using Gary Craig's Emotional Freedom Techniques.

Pre-Work

In many cases, before we can even begin to start, some pre-work needs to be done. It is the sad truth that many deep underlying beliefs we now have as adults about how children should be treated have been formed by the way WE were treated. Oh, indeed, we make decisions to "do much better than that" and many of us do when we are dealing with **other** children or our own; however, how we deal with **ourselves** remains often very much just like our caretakers did.

So, we might begin with asking some very basic questions about your feelings regarding "children" in total.

- How do you feel about children?

- Do you like them?

- Do you find them annoying, irritating, attention seeking, limiting to your own endeavours?

- Do you like **some types of children** better than others? If so, why?

- What types of children do you find particularly annoying? What age, type, gender, race, upbringing, looks?

- How do you feel about an adult's responsibility for the upbringing of children?

- Do you have any particularly strong views about what should or should not be done with, to or by children?

The questions above will begin to make you aware of some emotions and memories regarding children in general, including the recoil decision "not to go there at all" or "not being interested in children", for example.

If you are involved in personal development, either with clients or for your own healing and growth, and most likely, both, then "children" and their issues should really be of prime concern to you - naturally.

I don't have to tell you that most every long lasting problem or limitation now is rooted in some way in childhood experiences or the lack thereof, you already know this on every level.

So **should there be a resistance** to even looking into these kinds of issues, I would seriously ask you to have a tap on this very resistance - it could well contain a breakthrough key to your current problems.

Now, let us move on to working with your own past selves, the children that you once were.

Proxy Tapping Past Selves

The mechanism of proxy tapping is particularly useful in the context of IC healing approaches because it has a TRIPLE effect:

- Firstly, it clears the issue in question very successfully from the more resourceful, older position that you are now;

- Secondly, it creates a sense of **connection** and of **responsibility** for the past self - it is a form of **re-parenting** yourself.

- Thirdly, proxy tapping the past self both heals those old wounds and at the same time, changes the entire system that is your self esteem, self concept or whatever you want to call it, NOW as the changes ripple through the whole that is you, creating new templates of behaviour, thought and possibility as this happens.

Healing Through Time

I will make some suggestions now on possible areas where you might like to apply EFT, through time.

Conception & Pregnancy.

Consider the baby that was conceived and that would grow up to become you. What were the circumstances of this? Is there anything that comes to mind for this time period, any sense, any emotions, any words or statements you were told about that have stayed with you and still cause discomfort?

Example Opening Statements (please note the slight modifications in the statements):

- Even though this baby should never have been born, **I now** deeply and profoundly love and welcome this baby.

- Even though this baby was unwanted, **I now** deeply and profoundly love, accept **and welcome** this baby.

- Even though this baby's mother drank all through pregnancy, I now deeply and profoundly love and welcome this baby.

- Even though it was said that this baby was born under an unlucky star, I now deeply and profoundly love and welcome this baby.

You might like to do another round, after such statements have been completed, but use the generic set up statement of:

"I now deeply and completely HEAL this baby."

*Comment - If these Opening Statements cause you much distress, it might be best to do this process with another to help guide and support you.

Birth

Birth is always a very dramatic experience. You might remember something, you might have a feeling or sense of something that happened then, and many of us have been told many horrific things about this time, all of which is stored on some level in our multiordinate energy matrices.

Here are some example opening statements:

- Even though this baby caused his/her mother so much pain and suffering, I now deeply and profoundly forgive and love this baby.
- Even though this baby was born too early, I now deeply and profoundly love and accept this baby.
- Even though this baby nearly died, I now deeply and profoundly love and accept this baby.

Following the birth statements, I would advise to always append each round with a round of:

"I now deeply and profoundly heal this baby from all wounds he/she might have sustained at the time of birth."

0-6 Months

This is a critical stage in the life of a child, as it makes its first experiences with The Hard. Constant caretaking, attention, love, warmth, feeding is of the essence for this child to grow up strong and confident. There are those who say that the very most basic ideas and concepts, way below the threshold of conscious awareness or of words and pictures, are formed in that time.

Example Opening Statements:

- Even though this baby never received enough love, I now deeply and profoundly love this baby.
- Even though this baby was left alone in the dark, I now deeply and profoundly love and embrace this baby.

- Even though this baby was so helpless, I now deeply and profoundly love and accept responsibility for this baby.

- Even though this baby was always screaming, I now deeply and profoundly love and nourish this baby.

- Even though this baby never received enough of anything it needed, I now give everything to this baby.

I would advise to append each round with the following:

"I now deeply and profoundly heal this baby from the wounds he/she has sustained at that fragile time."

6 Months - 2 Years

Entirely reliant on the caretakers, the child now begins their own explorations of the World. Their experiences during this time - and this includes toilet training - are said to set their energy exchanges with the All There Is on a most profound level. This includes basic beliefs of what can and cannot be had, what can and cannot be done, what can and cannot be learned, as well as how, what and why relationships are constructed, mostly based on the primary caretakers of that time.

Example opening statements might include:

- Even though this child was not allowed to explore, I now deeply and profoundly love and encourage this child.

- Even though this child was ignored, I now deeply and profoundly acknowledge and love this child.

- Even though this child was totally overwhelmed by the world, I now deeply and profoundly love and take responsibility for this child.

- Even though this child was pushed on way too fast, I now deeply and profoundly love and accept this child.

Append as usual, any one given round with a round of:

"I now heal this child, deeply and profoundly, from all the injuries it sustained during this time of life."

226

2 Years - 6 Years

This is the time of development of the basic sense of self - who we are, what our place is in the world. Many very unhelpful self concepts are formed during this time, which may include first contacts with organised learning which are of the essence for undertaking a great many tasks that rely on learning and change in the future.

Example opening statements might include:

- Even though this child was a girl, I now deeply and profoundly love and accept this child.

- Even though this child was slow to learn, I now deeply and profoundly love and accept this child.

- Even though this child was said to have been "a little monster", I now deeply and profoundly love and accept this child.

- Even though this child was abused, I now deeply and profoundly love and treasure this child.

- Even though this child was different, I now deeply and profoundly love and treasure this child.

As always, append each round with the global:

I now heal all the injuries this child sustained during this time, deeply and profoundly, with my love.

And Onward To Maturity

Of course, change and learning do not stop when we are 6 years old. It would be most valuable indeed to continue on and create your own custom made line of growth beyond age 6 and into pre-teen, then teenager stage and until you have reached a point of conclusion where you felt maturity and adult hood had been obtained.

Now the truth is that many of us, age 40, 50, 60 and beyond have never really felt as though they did attain adulthood; many of us have a horror of such a state and actively fight it for many reasons, the main one being that those who were presented to us as models of adulthood were not what we would ever want to become.

However, it is my supposition that IC explorations, and more specifically, IC Healing can help accomplish this.

By taking responsibility in a true adult fashion - note, a true adult fashion not as was modelled by the so called "Grown Ups" around us - for our own selves, we are both healing past wounds as well as **recreating a whole new model** of adulthood for our own past selves.

This is a most profoundly healing and ecological set of energy exchanges **within our own self** that I absolutely believe needs to be accomplished FIRST and as the FIRST PRIORITY to any other endeavour.

For how can you heal others if you cannot heal yourself, how can you forgive others if you cannot forgive yourself, how can you serve others if you cannot serve yourself?

It is often said that "loving the self" precedes all endeavours to love others.

Loving the child you once were is an essential, if not **the only essential** component to understanding the nature of love, forgiveness and healing. I offer you these protocols for use with your self and your clients with my sincere wishes to you for deep healing and re-alignment.

The EFT "Needs & Wants" Protocol

Here is a nice pattern for those amongst you who are striving to achieve or attain something, or have been striving to achieve or attain something which may have eluded them so far, in spite of a considerable investment in time, prayer, therapy and tapping.

In general, it is so that consciously people WANT certain things or they think they want them, which amounts at the conscious level to much the same thing.

However, the entirety of our neurology is much more interested in what we NEED than what we want; and if there is a conflict between need and want, need tends to win out quite simply, every time, unless we can make it so that the want is perceived as a high order need, which is not something that I feel comfortable with doing for ecology reasons.

So, let us say a person wishes to be rich but they are poor.

They have done much therapy and personal development of one type or the other, but it hasn't changed to their satisfaction.

Please consider this to be a base pattern that is content free and insert your own (or your clients) statement of need on the topic of their choice instead.

The opening statement to discover the structures of the needs is as follows:

"I deeply and profoundly love and accept myself, even though I need to be poor."

This form handles numerous ereas all at the same time which include deservability issues of course, patterning (old memories) but most importantly, the **ecology** of the presenting problem.

It also allows for a break space of acceptance of the situation that is not asking for a change as yet and includes, very importantly, an admission of the problem being derived from a NEED as opposed to anything else, such as just being stupid, deranged, genetically or environmentally damaged, insane, self destructive or plain too lazy to have made the change already.

This is both a healing pattern in and of itself, as even the act of becoming aware of and openly acknowledging one's true NEEDS represents a major movement in systems which are often very stuck, very entrenched and very resistant to change or attempts to interfere with them; as well as opening the way for discovering more of how any one particular needs system is constructed and to reveal the order and sequence to resolving the system so it may flow freely once again.

In the course of the unfolding treatment, it is likely that identity issues, decisions, reversals and such are discovered which have created the situation of need (the need to defend, to survive, to be loved, to remain alive in spite of (...), etc). These can of course, be treated as normal; the outcome of the treatment is to have yourself or the client be aware of different ways to meet their core needs in new ways and a sense that they are able to do so, with a little trepidation perhaps but also with a great deal of excitement and joy.

S-L-O-W EFT

This is an application of the classic EFT protocol I have designed especially with self help in mind for complex or global issues."

Anyone who has used EFT for any length of time must know that sometimes it can happen that an issue has so many different layers and aspects, you think you will have to tap forever.

This is particularly the case if the topic is a high level nominalisation, such as "money", "happiness", "family", a person's name or your own name, or an illness you have had for a very long time - these kinds of words have so many different meanings, connotations and memories attached to them that you could easily generate a hundred opening statements or set ups and then some. When you are working by yourself, it can be most difficult to know where to start regarding a topic like that for the best effect, and I have even a suspicion that the main components to such a problem have a habit of hiding themselves from us.

Here is a simple way to use the basic EFT protocol with a single small variation involving time to release a great many aspects, whether you are aware of what they might be, or not.

Do the treatment for the psychological reversal on the sore spot or karate chop point, just saying the word or phrase you have chosen loudly and clearly, three times. There is no need to say anything else although you can always add, "I deeply and profoundly love and accept myself" if you wish to do so.

Then, start with the first treatment point, the eyebrow point, and tap it whilst you repeat the word or phrase out loud.

Stay on the point whilst you are thinking of things connected to the word or phrase; some people have memory flashes, some have just thoughts, others see pictures or just have physical sensations, it matters not. Keep tapping throughout, on that one point, and if any emotions appear, keep tapping that same point until they have gone. When the point feels as though it has been cleared, say the word again.

Often, more thoughts arise. If they do, stay on that point until they have all gone. Repeat until you have thoroughly "cleared" that part of your energy system, take a break, drink some water, and then go on to the next point, starting once again with the PR treatment, then go on to the corner of the eye point and repeat; do all the points used in EFT in that way, one at a time.

Depending on the word or phrase you are using, this might take a while and you might want to leave some of the points for the next treatment session with yourself.

We have tried this technique and have found it to be very helpful with long standing problems that have too many different aspects to even start, or problems you might have worked on for a long time and still you keep finding more and more aspects.

As a further support to really clear the issues around such a presenting problem, repeat the technique once a week for a month because sometimes, when shifts have taken place, whole new areas become apparent, much like an earthquake sometimes reveals ancient ruins you couldn't know were there before. On repeat treatments, many of the points remain clear and you get many fewer aspects emerging.

Should you come across a "heavy" memory or something you feel is of special importance in conjunction with your problem, you can make a note of it and treat it separately at another time with the full EFT protocol as well.

SLOW EFT In Brief

Slow EFT is used for complex problem gestalts and high level nominalisations, such as

- "money"
- "happiness"
- "family"
- a person's own name or another person's name
- an illness someone has had for a very long time.

These kinds of words have so many different meanings, connotations and memories attached to them that they could easily generate many hundred opening statements or set ups.

Slow EFT Protocol

1. Choose keyword or opening word or statement that describes the problem.

2. PR reversal correction on Sore Spot or KC point

3. Tap ONLY the first point until there is shift in experience or cognition and until all memory flashbacks and thoughts on the statement have been exhausted.

4. Repeat the keyword numerous times throughout the process.

5. Move on to the next point and repeat 1- 4 above.

Especially relevant thoughts and memories that occur during the Slow EFT process can be treated separately with any MET protocol.

The Channel Clearing EFT Protocol

This is a very thorough, very gentle "Channel Clearer" that may be used for overall restoration or deep release of a particular issue.

Even though it seems "slow" compared to a single EFT round for a problem, in actuality does not take longer than 10 – 15 minutes and represents a real experience for the client (or a self help user with initiative).

Centrally, there are **two** points being stimulated simultaneously, namely one point is being held all through the sequence of tapping all the points. This clears the channel and **the channel's relationships** to the other channels deeply on that particular presenting issue.

When this protocol is performed without an issue being presented, the technique represents an **overall channel clearing event** which is deeply relaxing and enjoyable.

As such the Channel Clearing protocol is a good choice for people suffering from chronic problems, are worn out or worn down by illness, depression or fatigue, as it does not require anything much from the client other than just to let it happen.

This protocol is designed for a second person to "do" with a first person. Please note that instead of the EFT tapping, the TAB version may be used whereby the point is not tapped but held, and the person instructed to take a deep breath in and out for each point through the sequence.

The client might like to close their eyes throughout the treatment.

1. Cover the area of the "Sore Spot" with the flat of your hand and with the other, stimulate all the points from the EFT sequence (including Gamut and KC) gently, moving quite swiftly from point to point.

2. When the round is complete, move on to the eyebrow point, holding this whilst stimulating once again, all the others. As before, continue holding the eyebrow point whilst stimulating one by one, one after the other, all the major EFT points and including the Gamut point. Remind the client to breathe deeply throughout the treatment.

4. Continue until all the points have had their turn to be "touched" for a whole round.

Please note that some of the points are centrally organised, namely the 3rd Eye Point, Under Nose and Under Mouth. These are just stimulated and "breathed into" when they appear in their own sequence; with all other points the opposing side is being stimulated whilst the other is being held, for example hold EB(left), tap/tab EB(right).

This protocol is probably more closely related to pure energy healing when it is being conducted **without** an opening statement or set up.

If an opening statement, issue or set up has been decided upon, it is the practitioner who gently speaks the reminder phrase. I would point out that for this protocol a very **generalised** opening statement is the most appropriate, such as "good health", "relaxation", "at ease" or something along those lines.

For more urgent or direct issues, the standard EFT protocol is a better choice; however, because the practitioner **bridges** the two points being stimulated during this protocol, it is more and other both than an ordinary EFT treatment and as such, often highly appreciated by clients for whom the business of healing, change and growth seems like a lot of hard work and who are in need of simple rest and restoration.

The EFT Shadow Emotions Protocol

As you might know, I am particularly interested when things don't work as the theory says they should, for it is my supposition that in the anomalies in any system, technique or theory the step up to the next level of understanding lies hidden.

Here is a jig saw puzzle piece for those who are interested in far ranging personal development and sweeping, global changes in their lives; who have experienced the effectiveness of METs to release emotional entanglements with certain subject matters; who have done a lot of work but for whom, mysteriously, their actual lives seem quite unchanged from where they started out.

When I use the term "actual lives" I mean measurable, physical, hard data, such as increased effectivity at work which should have resulted in promotion and a pay increase by now; or an increased ability to make close and loving relationships which one might measure in dinner invitations per calendar month or such.

To me, it is important to use such "hard" feedback devices for there are many ways to feel quite happy even when sitting on death row that are available to the human mind and I rather like to distinguish between effective **hard** strategies for change as opposed to mind changes that stay confined to the mind space and have no further repercussions than that.

It was interesting to observe that a percentage of people who use METs regularly, with a will, for personal development purposes were not actually getting the kind of cataclysmic shifts they had been looking for.

I have been wondering about this for a while, and it occurred to me the other day what a problem might well be, and how to go about solving it.

Treating Present Emotional Entanglements

It is a fact that unless an emotion or problem presents itself, we can't treat it.

Even the techniques that pass such things over to the unconscious mind for the sorting rely on a starting point where one would say, ok, this **is** the problem I want to work on.

To name the problem, one would, of course, by needs have to be aware that **there is a problem** - if one was entirely unaware that there was a problem, one could obviously not set the actions in motion needed to resolve this.

So what we are generally treating, either by ourselves or with a therapist, friend or a client, for that matter, are problems we are aware of and that have presented themselves.

I put forth the proposition that in some cases, the actual problems are not present at all and thus cannot be resolved and that the reason they are not present is because **the individual has structured their entire life in such a way that the problem need never be experienced**.

Holographic Emotions

A hologram doesn't show you a picture of what is there; rather by inference it shows you a kind of shadow of what must have been there in order to create this pattern you are actually seeing, much like a stone being dropped into a pond and even after it has disappeared, the ripples would tell you clearly exactly where once it was; if you were to dive there, you would find the exact stone.

Consider, for example, someone who suffers from agoraphobia.

If severe enough, they won't leave their house - ever - in order to not have to experience the intense panic this would cause.

This is a simple and blatant example. Such a person organises their entire life and that of their dependents and carers too around this problem to avoid having to feel that feeling. All forms of addictions are of course also examples of that category, as is the person who will take the stairs because they will have panic attacks in the lift.

238

However, they are of course well aware of "that feeling" at the conscious level and can thus present themselves for treatment.

What I call "shadow emotions" are the emotions we actually don't experience because we have constructed lives that protect us from ever having them in the first place, to the degree that we are entirely unknowing of their existence or of the terror we have of their experience in consciousness.

Tracking Back To The Original

Here are some questions to help elicit or track back towards someone's shadow emotions:

- What is unusual about your life compared to that of others?

- What do you do much more than other people?

- What do you do much less or even never at all?

- What decisions and behaviours don't make any sense about you to others yet they seem quite normal or even "the only possible way" for you?

- What is blatantly illogical about the way you have constructed your life across time to this where you are now?

- What areas of change are either seemingly entirely resistant or you haven't even ever considered to try and change at all?

And the final question is:

What emotion(s) must you never, never be allowed to experience (again)?

Likely Candidates

With a little bit of backward engineering and detective work, as you consider your own time line or that of others in its totality, you come up with likely candidates for these holographic, super-scary shadow emotions that really must not ever be experienced (or else ...).

I might make a short note that the or else ... is of the order of, or else I would die immediately, or else the world would stop, or else judgement day must arrive that instant.

Not particularly logical, but hey. When has the human neurology ever functioned in a linear Newtonian logical fashion?

So, we will have some likely candidates.

Failure perhaps, shame is always worth considering. Terror, sadness grief, - any description an individual would give of these "unbearable emotions". There are also some emotions which do not have a label at all and thus are particularly difficult in handling in consciousness. A classic example is the emotion related to the non-labelled, "Why did they do this to me?", which is neither sadness, nor fear, nor any other of the usual labelled categories.

I have found so far that there are probably two or three likely candidates, with one standing out clearly and drawing attention towards it strongly.

In the country of holographic emotions, that might well be the **least** frightening of them all, and that is alright because you have to start somewhere, and our neurology always looks out for us and wants to be sure that this is safe to do before letting us get any deeper into heavier territory.

Releasing Shadow Emotions

There are many ways to accomplish this. You can tap straight, on the fear of this emotion first, then the emotion itself. Of course, you can metaphorise the whole thing into numbers, shapes, gauges - feel free to use whatever approach seems the most natural.

It is possible that memories pertaining to the holographic emotion emerge; I am convinced that in order to basically censor these emotions out of a person's standard repertoire altogether and then to construct an entire incarnation around not having to experience them again, we are looking at some very highly charged memories indeed, probably from quite a young age (or also, if the time line has taken a major kink with a very noticeable "before" and "after" at any time in a person's life).

Results and Repercussions

Bearing in mind that I am talking about extreme emotions here and that shadow emotions may well set the boundaries and limits as to what an individual can ever hope to be, do or achieve (like the house would set the boundaries for the agoraphobic), I would propose that the restoration of the abilities of an individual to know that they can cope with future occurrences of these emotions will result in a measurable widening of their mental territory and correspondingly, their behavioural flexibility.

What I mean by that is that a person who has successfully treated a holographic or shadow emotion would find that they are behaviourally **and** mentally able to contemplate actions that were simply out of reach for them before - out of reach as in, entirely incomprehensible, entirely impossible, or simply not there at all as an option, like a missing hyperlink on an index page - the other page is there but you wouldn't know it and can never reach it.

I would close this with a health warning.

As I said already, the original causative processes that cause an entire set of feelings to be dropped from a person's life forever need to be very highly charged.

You are dealing with very volatile material that needs to be handled with great care and concern, especially when working with clients.

The Shadow Emotions intervention should not be undertaken with a client unless they are absolutely ready and willing and the concept has been explained. I would personally not even start with a Shadow intervention unless I was sure the client responded readily and positively to MET treatments to get them out of trouble if the original causative processes were highly traumatic, probably had not been available to consciousness for many years, or if the client was fragile or unstable.

The Instant EFT Protocols

Just as someone who practises Karate will find that their body seems to learn blocking and protection movements to become entirely automatic, reflexive and unconscious after a time, someone who practises EFT will find that their body can learn to do a treatment all by itself if it is instructed to do so.

This is essentially the experience of many advanced EFT users, namely that they have only to think or say the words "Even though ..." and that is quite enough for yawning, tearing of the eyes, energy shifts and body sensations to become apparent without having tapped on a single point.

I have experienced this too of course and I have also seen a number of clients who would express a negative emotion, decide to tap on it, raise their hand to the Sore Spot or reach over for the Karate Chop tap, stopped in mid movement and started to laugh as the whole thing had already happened, all by itself.

Instant EFT works best when:

- The person who uses it has familiarity with the Classic EFT protocol;
- they trust the Classic EFT protocol to unblock/re-align their systems;
- and they have little or no blockages in their internal communications with the energy body/body mind which would preclude the ability of the body mind to do this from working.

Therefore, and once again, "learning" Instant EFT is not so much a question of acquiring new skill sets or a lot of practise, but far more a question of unblocking the **natural abilities** of our own totalities to get on and do what they were designed to be doing for us in the first place.

Now, let us make it as easy as possible for all concerned to re-learn how we set up our totality systems for self treatment which is of course what Instant EFT is in essence.

Unblocking The Self Treatment Systems

Limiting beliefs and meanings are the usual suspects to stop the self treatment systems to come into operation.

Whether you are teaching or learning IEFT, we thereby start with any contra-indications an individual may have and treat these with Classic EFT to get them out of the way:

- This would be too easy
- Other people might be able to do this but not me
- I don't believe it can be done like this
- IEFT won't work as well as physical tapping
- You need to physically stimulate the body to make the energy system respond.

... or whatever else you or the client might be thinking to stop it all from proceeding most smoothly.

Communicating Intent To The Body Mind

Now, we have a body mind which is willing and ready to perform an "EFT Rebalancing" or major meridian clearing session as and when instructed.

What we need next is to communicate our intent to have this be done to the body mind.

As we think a great many things at the rate of knots all day long and at night when we sleep, the body mind as all the unconscious systems are basically programmed to ignore all and everything we come up with unless the message is marked out in some way as being relevant.

As the attempted act of giving oneself post hypnotic suggestions in the form of affirmations and all sorts of other avenues has been attempted already by most people with very dubious results, half heartedly and against the energy blockages which exist to stop anything much from happening, simply stating the intention is not as effective as it might have been once upon a time when things were very different altogether.

I therefore suggest to perform a symbolic action to support the instruction that the EFT style major meridian clearance on the top is to take place on top of the general instruction with will and voice that it should be so.

Naturally, the Sore Spot, being always the first point in any EFT treatment **chain** is the prime candidate for this symbolic action, as the totality is already well used to this being the starting point for the forthcoming release.

So here is what we do:

1. Place your entire hand over the sore spot (either side will do but preferably, hand on your heart :-), wait until you can feel the warmth of your hand on your skin and gently move the hand in a circular motion.

2. State out aloud that when you place your hand there and think about a problem, starting with the words "Even Though ..." you would like the EFT sequence on the topic in question to take place immediately and automatically.

3. Take your hand away, take a deep breath (break state) and think of a problem in order to contact it.

4. Now, place your hand on your heart and say the opening statement out aloud. Pay attention to what happens next – your physical sensations. Is something happening?

5. The first few times you do this, you might find that the process gets started but stops somewhere. You can help your fledgling IEFT process along by giving a gentle tap where it seems to have become stuck and then letting it take its own course again.

6. Practise IEFT until it noticeably happens quite fast and all by itself.

There is no harm or problem if you sometimes still have to tap a few points here and there to **support the unfolding learning** of the energy body how to do this and what it is that you want it to be doing.

Some topics need this, especially when you first start with IEFT.

Progression To Pure IEFT

At first, we will always keep our hand on the heart because this is the absolute, no mistake, physiological instruction to the body mind which will always take physiological evidence in preference to thoughts of intention (hence the importance of congruency in mind body states to get anything important done and supported by the unconscious mind and the general totality).

We also keep the "even though" trigger in place for each treatment, even if we are just concentrating on a feeling that needs to be released, are looking at an object or using any other kind of attunement device to the problem including silence.

You will find that the EFT meridian channel clearing will process much faster than you could ever physically tap it; and that the process becomes more profound and more profoundly noticeable with just a little practise.

To move towards pure IEFT, please, don't be impatient. Don't rush it and give yourself the time you need to really have learned the basics and it works reliably, gets stuck rarely and you can really feel the shifts.

There is absolutely no merit in pushing towards these next stages if the underlying basics have not fully been learned – all that will happen is not a saving in time, but that you end up with a self healing system that is crippled and never as effective for you as it could have been.

When you are ready, and no sooner than that, you can begin to:

1. Think the trigger of "even though" instead of speaking it out loud;

2. Next, leave the trigger out and just focus your intention on what needs to be treated. But please note that if it fails to work, immediately back up and practise the "even though" stage for a little while longer.

When you can really feel the clearing running straight through your systems when you just hold your hand to your heart and focus on the disturbance, we are ready to let go of the last help device in learning IEFT, namely physically placing your hand on your heart.

To begin this what in fact is a quantum leap in your ability to communicate with your body mind directly and instantly, we make the intention of putting our hand on our heart by focussing on the act of doing it **but not actually performing the action itself**.

You might need to help this process along, once again, at the beginning by at least beginning the gesture in physicality to bridge between the physical instruction and the pure intention.

When you can create that stateshift by intention, namely the state where the body mind is alert and ready to go, waiting for the next instruction, namely what to focus on for the actual clearing, you and your body mind have learned a number of very important things indeed, and not least of all, how body mind/conscious mind communication works – namely with stateshift and intention, focussed and controlled.

As such, and once again, EFT has shown itself to be a fantastic training and teaching device that bridges between physicality and intent and for this single purpose, it is very well worth it to make the slight effort it takes to really learn how to do IEFT as excellently and elegantly as we were designed to be able to do.

EFT Shamanic Applications

No matter how some might like to turn EFT into something strictly mechanical and Newtonian, with talk of batteries, power lines, circuits and so forth, the fact is that EFT is a quantum realms based form of change intervention.

The meridian system we are happily tapping on is not visible and not measurable by current devices; its effects on various parts of the physiology can just about be measured but not the meridians themselves.

Neither can the even more invisible components of the energy body such as chakras, thoughtfields, energetic shields, bonds and fields and so forth; and so really, the moment someone starts to tap they are already knee deep in this esotericism, if only they knew it.

I don't actually know who was the first person to come up with the idea of "proxy treatments" – most likely a Kinesiologists because they are familiar and comfortable with the idea of "muscle testing by proxy". It came first to my attention when I was told about a lady whose newborn and very premature baby was dying. No-one expected the tiny boy to last the night, and the lady couldn't touch him for tubes and in the glass case in which he lay so she sat outside and tapped all night – mostly for her own sadness and fear and to transmit her support and love for him in any way she could, with no possibility of physical contact.

In the early hours of the morning, the tiny boy began to brighten and not only did he live through the night, he went on to grow and develop strongly and was duly released to his parent's care much sooner than was usual for such babies.

Since then, proxy treatments have become a well known but perhaps slightly uncomfortable part of EFT treatments as EFT is still being sold as simple and mechanical in order not to frighten off the many people who would not touch anything more metaphysical with a barge pole.

Here are the main points of Proxy Work in brief before we begin with the more advanced applications.

Proxy (Surrogate) Work

Proxy Treatments can be performed for:

- Another person
- An animal
- A person who is no longer alive
- A part or sub-personality of a person
- A problem, problem group
- An illness or disease
- "Entities" such as corporations, oceans, entire population groups
- Ideas, concepts, constructs and powerfields.

The True Proxy Set Up Statement

"I AM (insert target name or description)."

This is a shamanic style identification and very powerful indeed. In dropping the barriers to that which seeks healing and aligning with it, getting into rapport so deeply that there is no longer the distinction between self and that other, the self treatment **becomes** the healing for the other.

There are many more aspects to this base process; please see "The Vortex" for an in-depth explanation of why this dissolution of barriers between self and other are so very powerful in discovering the truth about a disturbance and what is needed to heal it.

What is interesting is that simple, classic EFT with a user who has no idea of shamanic laws and procedures and no particular skill or ability to make that **move** into the other in consciousness or with any kind of volition will give noticeable and often excellent results just by the simple phrasing of "I am (this person, this problem, this animal)".

Changing Perceptional Positions

Changing perceptional positions on the problem and treating it from this other point of view rather than from the ordinary state-self allows for leverage on problems that cannot be resolved otherwise.

The most commonly known of these perceptional moves in EFT proxy treatments is this form of Third Person opening statement:

"Even though (insert target) (has this problem), I deeply and profoundly love and accept (target)."

This is a very interesting treatment approach for stuck problems or if there is a sense that an important piece of information is missing, which, if it was known or contactable, would resolve the presenting problem entirely.

Numerous different positions can be taken on one single target, for example:

"Even though Sarah has this problem ..."

"Even though she has this problem ..."

"I am Sarah. Even though I have this problem ..."

"I am Sarah's mother. Even though Sarah has this problem ..."

"I am Sarah's higher self. Even though Sarah has this problem ..."

Treating Aspects Of Self

Clearly from the section above it follows that any individual engaging in parts work can use the various forms of shifting from one to another for exploration, treatment or healing would find tremendous benefits from proxy tapping.

In the "Pearls Pattern", for example, named after Fritz Pearls, the creator of Gestalt therapy, one can shift into the angry mother part and tap from there as the angry mother would and thereby release the mother's anger from the energy field of the actual client. This is a very powerful form of intervention and deeply healing and re-balancing.

Conflicting parts and sub-personalities can be treated for their own shortcomings, fears and limitations just as successfully as to have their owner treat the parts in question.

One of the core applications of shamanic work is of course, Soul Retrieval. Now whether a client uses the framework of Soul Retrieval instead for parts work or whether they are really trying to retrieve parts of their souls is actually immaterial; any objections or blockages to allowing a part of the soul to return home may be soothed away with the application of EFT, IEFT or Slow EFT.

It is always important to remember that EFT proxy work is absolutely quantum based - there are no limitations on size, distance and time (important in working with the past and the future, such as healing processes involving people who are already dead or circumstances, events and experiences which are irretrievably lost).

Quantum Time & Space EFT Treatments

There is a range of manifestations which might have a therapist or healer think more of exorcism than EFT but the fact is that EFT can very successfully deal with disturbances – and indeed, it matters not where they reside, how they come to be, if they are imaginary or if we are dealing with real relationships, memories, entities etc.

The fact is that people and their problems and relationships are a structural puzzle and that the structure of the problems is usually the same, whether we are dealing with a suspected demonic possession or a spider phobia. By using EFT which is a very practical and "sensible" approach which further, does not install more confusion because it simply treats what is already there, we have a set of approaches to the most very esoteric of presenting problems which keep the whole thing balanced and provide outstanding opportunity for success.

The rule in all such esoteric dealings, be it with past lives, dead people, past events, powerfields, entities, demons, attachments, angels, higher selves, karmic and prophetic notions, dream messages, enlightenment events and more besides is to proceed **exactly** as though we were dealing with real life events in all ways.

So, rather than to question whether a woman who seeks help with negative emotions about her husband actually has one or is just making the whole relationship up for the purpose of deflecting from a more important problem, we likewise do not question whether or not a past life or a demon or a spirit attachment etc. etc. is real or not, but simply proceed with the treatment based on what the client says is troubling them and as is prescribed clearly in the Classic EFT protocol.

Fascinatingly, sometimes it turns out that the entity etc. wasn't the real problem at all – but then, that often happens with spider phobias and eating disorders too, so that's nothing either new or spooky.

Other times, it clearly was and to treat the whole relationship and the feelings of the client in the context simply does the trick to resolve the problem – and it is the client who is doing the problem resolution, something so profoundly exciting and useful, we should remember what a bonus EFT treatments are in that respect.

Memory and imagination, at any rate, are quantum in nature anyway and no matter what else might or might not be real about our new and developing maps of the Universe.

Someone who is still entangled in a powerful relationship with a person who has already been dead for many years is practically just as entangled as someone who is having a relationship with a demon.

So, and rather than suggesting opening statements for EFT treatments for "esoteric occurrences", here is one more time the key to all of this work and this is to take what the client says exactly "as is" and to treat it exactly like we would treat any other memory, relationship, addiction, fear of (...), and all the emotions relating to the context matter.

Working With EFT In DreamTime

Clearly, this is not the kind of pattern one would offer a client off the street who wishes to release their spider phobia and nothing more.

However, there are many amongst us who are both fascinated with and deeply involved with more in-depth magical and shamanic approaches.

The most central and most important of those is to work in DreamTime (or in Sanctuary, in the causal planes, in Serein or whatever term is being used for the magical spaces which lie at the interface between the physical and the quantum realms of silence)

Now you may think that simple little EFT is nowhere near holy and esoteric enough to be of any use in these exalted realms, and you'd be very wrong to think that indeed.

Every shamanic teacher over the ages worth their salt has said time and time again that **every human being** can reach DreamTime, work in DreamTime and gain the benefits from this – even though societies through the ages have severely restricted access to the chosen few.

Anyone who reads this and has worked in these spaces will know that more often than not, one finds oneself standing there and simply having no idea at all what is expected, what one should do or what one should do next. Usually, this is accompanied by a real sense of frustration and the profound sense that we **do know** all about these realms, could do what we wanted if only we could somehow remember how it all worked and what we were supposed to be doing here.

What we have here are exactly the same kind of energetic disturbances and blockages which would preclude an affirmation from working, or stop someone from learning as fast and furiously as humans were designed to learn – the same thoughtfields, constructs, shields, energetic injuries (which show up as fears and doubts) is what we take right with us when we work **consciously** in the magical realms and quantum spaces and they can be released here just as easily and profoundly as they can be when someone is sitting in a real hard traffic jam and having a panic attack.

An intention to remove the disturbances is often all that is required, and for any EFT user, the thought of **doing EFT** translates in the magical realms **directly** into an instruction to have this be done swiftly right now. It is true that a familiarity but perhaps more importantly, a deep sense of trust in one's abilities to make IEFT work will come in very handy in order to overcome perceived limitations and old blockages to working **naturally** in the magical spaces.

The EFT Vortex Pattern

This EFT pattern that allows you to take a new perspective on your "problems" and in doing so, opens new lines of communication within the Self on which healing can travel in a whole new way.

As I am sure you already know, healing or to use that other expression, creating Even Flow is **NEVER A WAR**.

It is a natural enough human reflex given the ins and outs of our societal entrainments to think of healing as winning and dying as losing, for example. That's fairly obviously a limitation and most healers have understood that consciously as well as having known it to be true unconsciously forever anyway.

It is not so directly obvious and more insidious, if you will, when we talk about "losing the battle against cancer" or "fighting off an infection" or "holding out against the ravages of (insert disease)".

In medical terminology, war metaphors abound. They are everywhere and they clearly indicate that all of us are entrained most profoundly to view pain and illness and problems and symptoms of all kinds as "the enemy" that needs to be "vanquished".

The trouble with this is that if you view wellness as a war, you've lost before you ever fired your first arrow or struck the first blow with your lance because inevitably you will just die and lose in the end, and so will all your patients, your clients, their loved ones and everyone else, including the stars themselves at some point in the future.

Very depressing, isn't it.

But there's more to that. The metaphor of "war" brings with it serious limitations, especially in the communications department - what kind of communications can be had with an enemy who is all out to kill you in the end can be mostly numbered on the pads of a couple of paws, and as to the energetic "flavour" of any interaction between two parties at war – well ....

That could not possibly be what we would consider Even Flow. Or unconditional love, or seeing the light within, or basic compassion nor any of all these other precepts we have now accepted as being absolutely fundamental to making the systems that we are, that the animals are, that the Earth is, that the universe itself is on all the planes and levels work together as beautifully and harmoniously as they were originally designed to function.

We are therefore going to seriously consider an illness or energetic disturbance as **an entity that has a right to be here** and deserves to be treated with exactly the same unconditional regard, respect and compassion as we need to extend to the rest of creation and ourselves included if we want to live successfully and to our full potential in the Hard. I appreciate that at the level of the Hard this is often not an easy thing to do, if it is possible at all or even meant to be done at the level of the Hard. I am sure you have heard it be said that emotional involvement with a patient is a hindrance to healing rather than a help. This is correct of course and an observation made by all healing modalities over all of mankind's endeavours in this area.

However, what is not being told is just how you are supposed to accomplish this. There is a much loved being, they are in pain, they are calling to you for help and you are hurting with them, hurting for them, scared to death that they will die and you're going to be left by yourself and not being able to stand the pain of it, and you are supposed to be "not emotionally involved"????

Sadly, many healers take this advice to heart and build barriers around themselves or dis-associate themselves from their feelings, becoming hard and bitter and desperately dis-satisfied in the process as their true healing skills in turn become cut off and walled away and thus cannot express themselves. There is a structural way out of this, namely to understand that emotional involvement is absolutely correct and as it should be in the Hard but that when you move up the planes where the much loved creature becomes an energy system and you the shuttle in the weaver's hand that repairs the threads, those emotional Hard aspects drop away automatically because you are working in an entirely different space altogether where emotions are not at all like those of the Hard and your love and compassion for those you are wanting to help is all there is - naturally and without even having to work at it!

It is here, too, that other types of emotional involvements **such as the hatred for the disease and its effects** drop away and you can see the disease or disturbance for what it really is - an existing energetic reality, a part of the universe, a being in its own right that has its own needs and purposes and that, if understood and listened to can tell you exactly and specifically what needs to be done to have it be other, elsewhere, or simply in peace and oh so gently dissolve to the night sky.

Healing The Vortex with EFT

1. Tune into your body/situation as it is right now and let your thoughts go to a problem, challenge, pain, an emotion or an issue that is drawing your attention.

2. What would you call this? Give it a name. For this exercise we are going to use "My Problem".

3. Have an idea of how "big" the problem is - give it a rating between 0 and 100, so that we have a clear conscious knowing of how it has changed beyond how different it feels after the treatment.

4. Start the normal EFT exercise with PR correction and the opening statement of: "I am (my problem) and I deeply and profoundly love and accept myself." This is the normal EFT proxy protocol.

*It is perfectly ok to say "the" problem instead if that feels more appropriate.

4. On the points, as you tap, you repeat, "My (the) problem".*

*As you tap on each point, and if it should happen, you can add something about the statement that comes to mind. That often takes care of "aspects" there and then and reduces the amount of rounds necessary to entirely resolve the situation.

5. At the end of the round, take a new reading. Also notice if you need to **re-name** your problem for a subsequent round or if the original problem is the same only milder/less now. Sometimes they shift and become something else entirely but not always.

6. After you have finished, take a moment to just sit quietly and reflect on what you have thought, felt, experienced and learned about the nature of your problem.

NB: You can do this pattern proxy for another person, the set up being, "I am (Danny's)(problem)."

EFT In The Bereavement Flow

Bereavement is one of those issues that cannot help but set up a resonance to one's own bereavements, moments of such intense sadness and if you will, emotional suffering that it is understandable why we might want to back away from thinking about such things so we can keep ourselves evenly balanced and functioning in the Hard.

It is also understandable that humans have tried to make the suffering of bereavement easier somehow throughout the ages in many different ways.

Every society has rituals to help them deal with the tearing up of energetic connections on so many levels and layers that occur when an individual that was in a relationship with another ceases to be – and when I say every society, I include in that societies of animals too, from bees to elephants, primates, feral cat groups and dolphins.

Here are the main points to consider in the context of "bereavement as an energetic occurrence".

1. Death is the Ultimate Catastrophe for the physicality.

2. It is the final step on a smooth progression from birth to death, but not perceived like that amongst humans.

3. The physicality will do **everything** to remain intact and it never gives up this single minded task.

4. At the energetic levels, the connector planes and up, bereavement is the most serious energetic injury any individual (animals and humans) can undergo.

5. Bereavement is a **naturally occurring process** that normally progresses in a set pattern but The Hard being what it is, has many possibilities of producing long lasting, and possibly fatal, energetic injuries in all concerned.

Bereavement As An Energetic Injury

In many ways, bereavement injuries and the severe, severe responses that individuals have to this form of injury **only make sense** when viewed at the energetic level.

In the Hard, bereavement doesn't make sense in many cases at all. After all, the absence of a something that was there before is often very much "a blessing" at that level – no more hard work, no more trouble, no more problems with that individual. Take them out and your world's a better place, your life will be better and you will be happier all around.

But also in the Hard, the results are not like that.

What we have is severe immune system responses indicative of highest levels of stress, for one.

A highly statistically significant proportion of people who develop cancer had **a serious bereavement in the two years** preceding the first diagnosis.

The fact is that most humans after a serious bereavement show a multitude of neuro-somatic illnesses of all kinds.

As we said before, bereavement of another energy system one had many connections with is a very serious business and the highest end of these kinds of injuries and therefore, we can use them to demonstrate and easily perceive what an incredible blow to the entirety of someone's being bereavement represents.

And as we said before, bereavement is not just about death.

It occurs under many other circumstances and the easiest way to spot this type of injury is to consider the individual and their energetic connections in context.

I would like you to consider any circumstance where **energetic connections are torn, cut or broken** and systems made up of many multi-parts are being pulled apart, as a form of bereavement. This includes therefore everything one has relationship with, and including objects, animals, lovers, landscapes and not just the act of destruction or death but also events such as moving away, breaking up, getting sick, changing dramatically and becoming therefore, another and so forth.

Here is a visualisation for you:

You could consider an individual – an imaginary, perfect, template type of individual! – to look something like this on the energetic levels. Actually, I **do** imagine them to look like this, right down to the silver core of the Unchanging You and beyond that into the ultra-dimensions of the Immortal Beloved that I cannot visualise anymore.

Here is a delightful picture of two such individuals interacting energetically:

As you can see, although there are absolutely two individuals there, it is virtually impossible to say where one ends and where the other starts.

Now, there is the third picture, that of pulling two individuals apart:

There is the catastrophe, clearly visible, as the pulling away of the smaller individual on the bottom right totally distorts the shape and integrity of the main individual that once looked much more like pictures 1 or 2.

You can imagine that the further the second individual pulls away, the longer and finer these strands that extend from one to the other become until they will break, and some parts will be drawn back into the individual in time; hopefully, it will regain its original shape or near enough.

- We too have systems – such as the gravity arrangements for these fields of stars in the pictures – to help us re-shape our energy systems even after a major disarrangement or catastrophe.

This is in visual terms and using the beautiful galaxies to illustrate this, is how bereavement of any kind should be experienced on the part of the individual that remains here in the Hard in physicality.

The Energetic Stages Of Bereavement – Working With The Causes

The four main stages of Shock, Awareness, Healing, and Renewal in terms of our Galaxy model of interaction and bereavement makes perfect sense energetically.

To back up, here is what happens energetically and all the "stages of bereavement" and their details are simply the symptoms of the energetic disarray:

Shock

This is systemic overload. Too many systems are on red alert at once and collapse the interface devices designed to act in some pro-active way to maintain Even Flow. Systemically, this is a necessity to be able to maintain any form of functioning at all.

Energetic Intervention For Shock

What you will find is that the core systems of any individual in shock are walled around and have withdrawn tightly inside. Please note that it is very dangerous to bring or attempt to bring out such an individual by force. It can lead to severe systemic overload (irreparable mental damage, coma, autism, heart attack, stroke).

You may, however, side-step the energetic disarray and contact the individual **inside** their protective castle walls and there, give them strength, compassion, or whatever you perceive is the right "flavour" of energy at this their time and state of being.

Often, simply contacting an individual who is in shock on that level will give them a sense of not having been abandoned altogether, of not being alone in the universe, and hope. Hope is one of those indescribable energy states that money can't buy and that is the candle flame in the darkness that makes a whole lot of other processes even begin to be possible at all, including eventual healing and emergence.

EFT Treatments For Shock

Remember that the main feature is systemic overload. This is probably not a good time for targeted opening statements; tapping in silence, the Channel Clearer and Slow EFT are the best option. Also, simply holding a hand to the Sore Spot can help with the many systems in reversal and just to steady in physicality for a time.

Treating another who is in shock with Proxy EFT is very helpful. Once again, rather than being to specific, very global opening statements ("Mary's husband has died.") are preferable; if any attunement to the other's energy system shows nothing but shock, blankness and stand still, silent support is perfect too.

Awareness

This would be the moment when the survivor emerges finally from their bunker and surveys the ruin of their lands and home after the catastrophe.

It is overwhelming. No other words for it. In the galaxy model, the tearing away has happened and you can see bits flying here and there, the whole system out of shape and open, pouring out rather than feeding back in itself, everything in disorder and disarray.

If you were to pull up a standard psychology list of emotional problems associated with this stage, every single so called negative human emotion is there at full strength and these are the indicators of this energetic disarray.

Energetic Interventions For Disarray & Awareness

This individual perceives themselves to be "all in pieces" and energetically speaking, they are correct. However, there are still the central core systems of the individual and once again, these are the first ones to find, to contact and to strengthen. Indeed, bringing these to any individual's awareness by simply touching them or speaking with them, if you will, is the pre-requisite to maintaining the situation and **before** going to the outside systems and beginning any repairs there.

Once again, the ecology warning. This is a natural tide of things we are dealing with here. There is no merit whatsoever in forcefully pushing systems back into place (even if you could) – all that would do is to create even more disarray.

However, tuning into the process, becoming aware of just where it is in the expansion/stretching/tearing/disarray/re-assembling progression and smoothing that progression along (more of this later) and **supporting** the unfolding processes is a fantastic and incredibly healing energetic intervention.

EFT Statements For Awareness

Naturally arising "chaos" statements are in general the most helpful ones at this stage: "I am in pieces." – "My heart is broken." – "I feel as though I died too." – "I don't know who I am anymore." – "I just don't know what to think or do." or whatever the person says to describe this state allows a general calming effect when the opening statement is used.

What happens with EFT treatments when you do this is that the client accesses the major underlying injuries which are causing the disarray much faster than we are used to in our experience of treating or helping others with bereavement. As you work with this, bear in mind that this is a good thing and will allow an individual to recover much, much faster and with much less possibilities of retaining severe long term damage from the energetic event of bereavement.

Healing

The galaxy, pulled slowly back into its original shape by forces of gravity, is now beginning to re-establish its own natural ecology. It is fragile still and not familiar yet with the new states of being and the new order of things in the absence of what used to be and what used to prescribe the old states of being by its presence and its interactions and so it needs a time to adjust.

Energetic Interventions For Healing

In general, there is really very little that needs to be done to an energy system in this stage other than to offer a little light support and encouragement – a light vibration, a very light touch so as not to unbalance it again or stop the processes of metamorphosis that are taking place.

The individual might have well constructed a barrier around themselves, not like the thick castle walls of shock but more like a space, or distance, like an egg shell or the cocoon of an about to emerge butterfly. If you perceive any clear breaches in this cocoon, by all means very gently fix it to help the new galaxy within be able to complete its re-organisation in safety.

EFT Statements For Healing

What we really need to be the most aware of in this stage is anything at all that could **block** the processes of healing – it is at this stage where the most lasting damage occurs as some systems never find their way back to how they should be functioning and remain stuck in a chaotic state.

Emotional pain of any kind can now directly be targeted as something that stands in the way of the individual's long term health, and whatever predominant emotions are being expressed by the client can now be treated directly.

It is very helpful if at all possible to explain to a client (or to remember yourself) that being in a constant state of pain with no evolution and forward movement into healing and Even Flow is **NOT NATURAL** and not in any way as God, the world, the universe, or their loved one ever intended.

They are strange beliefs in people's minds about needing to prove how deep their love or connection was to the object or subject of bereavement by suffering as profoundly as they loved and these, too, make profound blockages to the natural healing process. Beliefs such as, "If I don't live in constant agony at this loss, it will mean that I never loved him at all." – "The pain is better than to have no connection to him left." and similar ideas can all effectively block the essential process of healing – for an entire life time.

Emergence or Renewal

When the above re-organisation is completed, the individual emerges and is ready to make new relationships with other individuals. The protective barriers dissolve and the process of touching and getting closer to another, weaving with them, making them be a part of you and losing them again repeat as the seasons follow one another in the Hard.

EFT Statements For Emergence

People are very unaware of the energetic shields and barriers they have built around themselves and so, they really don't know that these need to be taken down again at some point.

Especially if a client brings an old bereavement, a bereavement that was not treated by an Energy Therapist from the start but got stuck before the emergence and renewal state was completed, chances are that there are major unhealed pains behind this shielding which cause meanings to be made of the "I will never survive having to go through this again – no more relationships for me, ever." variety.

As you can see, this follows on quite naturally from the meanings at the Healing stage – as long as someone thinks that they will lose their last connections and memories of the loved one by letting go of the pain, or that they are being disloyal by forming new relationships, these barriers absolutely cannot come down.

Here then you find the last reasons why an emergence cannot be contemplated, must not be desired, is not allowed to take place and these become the opening statements for EFT treatments to really complete the healing. In your investigation with the client, centre on the possibilities of new relationships of the same or possibly even more profound intensity. When you propose this, the client will tell you why such a thing is impossible and they have to remain alone, at home and behind their barriers for ever – those are the blockages to true renewal.

The Cycle Of Relationships

Now, the truth is that the Even Flow of making and breaking relationships as described above does not always proceed in this way. People get stuck in one or the other of these phases and problems can occur at any stage; think of the equivalent of a wound becoming infected rather than healing cleanly, for example.

Also, environmental conditions play a very important part in this relationship cycle – an egg won't hatch if it is too cold, for example – and, of course, our model galaxy is involved in many, many such relationship cycles in various stages **all at the same time**.

When dealing with bereavement related problems, for energy healers these are the main considerations:

1. To be absolutely clear that it isn't our job to "make it all better" but to further, support and smooth out the naturally existing processes of the Cycle of Relationships.

2. To be aware of just where an individual is in the Cycle; and

3. To spot **obstacles** to completing the Cycle successfully and to treat those.

Obstacles To Completing The Cycle Of Relationships

Imagine a rubbery substance in the shape of a ball. You pick up a part between finger and thumb and pull it out, stretch it, stretch it more.

At some point, one of three things occurs:

1. Either, you lose your grip and the stretched out line gets drawn back into the ball; or

2. the ball just follows and flies forward to the source of the pull; or

3. the stretched strand breaks and you end up with a small piece of the rubber substance in your hand, a distance away and fully detached from the original object.

Option 1 is the equivalent of a natural bereavement healing; No. 2 is the equivalent of dying of a broken heart, and No 3 is the most common energetic long term injury that stops bereavement processes unfolding to an Even Flow conclusion and what causes the most problems with animals and people alike.

Depending of how much of any given individual was so deeply invested in the other, or just accidentally became too far away from the original galaxy to be returned by gravity when the final separation occurred, these "lost parts" represent a very important form of energetic injury indeed, and one, if healed or corrected through our interventions, will have a tremendous impact on the system that is the client as a whole.

Energetically speaking, there is no such thing as a "clean break" – there is some form of resonance connection always remaining amongst all the parts of our galaxy that precludes healing on the one hand, and is a constant reminder and source of disturbance and loss on the other.

"Retrieving" A Lost Part

Here, we are dealing with a belief that precludes a part of the energy system to return to the energy body as it should – a "hole" in the person's energy body, if you will.

It is extraordinary how much power a person's conscious decisions and reflex-like meaning making devices have at the energy body levels to stop a natural healing process in its tracks and literally keep parts of their own self outside in the cold which would simply return quite naturally if there was no such guidance mechanism.

Often, people with severe bereavement problems express the idea that "something died with the other" – their ability to love, to have faith and trust, to enjoy life, or much more specific resources, desires and abilities, such as the will to live, the desire to dance, the dream of one day living in Spain, the idea to write a book and so forth.

The fascinating aspect of treating for this with EFT is that it soon becomes crystal clear that these "parts" were never lost at all and that they need no retrieving, either – with the blockages out of the way, they simply come flooding home with no problems at all, once their owners have arrived at a point where they may allow themselves to remove the objections to their homecoming.

Returning What Does Not Belong

The second most common energetic problem is exactly the opposite to that of the lost parts – namely, lost parts of the deceased other remaining in the system and causing havoc because they don't belong there.

This is a most fascinating thing on every level. Often, the two individuals involved in the bereavement scenario align in this – the one about to die doesn't want to go and will gladly **give a part of themselves** to the other, who doesn't want to be left without them and is holding on to them as best they can from their end, for **safekeeping** and to defy the Ultimate Catastrophe in a way.

In high magic, and between two individuals who know what they are doing, this is a powerful process that has many **positive** benefits and uses; when it happens chaotically and as a part of the disarray of the detachment, it can seriously unbalance the systems of the one who remains alive in physicality.

Anyone who has had a very intense relationship prior to the death/removal of the other is a candidate to be suffering from these "traded parts". Should you find such a thing, you have three options:

1. Do nothing and leave well alone. Especially with two individuals aligning on some level to do this type of trade, there may be more going on that meets our understanding at this level. If you get a feeling that you are in the presence of something unusual and holy in spite of the suffering of the individual, it might be time to back up and to just offer gentle steadying and support.

2. Facilitate the "part that doesn't belong" to go home as well and join the rest of the system in death by dealing with the relationship strands that hold it in place still such as the "reasons" for needing or wanting this part and what it would mean if it went away.

3. Find a way for the part to become fully integrated into the systems of the recipient and to be a resource rather than an infection.

Further Obstacles To Even Flow Bereavement

If you consider the Cycle of Relationship in the Even Flow as it was probably designed energetically in the first place for creatures living in more or less the same environment and with more or less the same family of creatures around them, you can already pre-suppose some of the places at which things might go awry.

One of these is surprise and shock over accidental or unexpected death.

As there is no time for the systems to begin to disentangle step by step, it is a particular incidence of fast upheaval all across the levels. There is a terrific sense of confusion as to what happened and a corresponding long term energetic confusion as to how safe it ever is anywhere for any part of the system which, as you can imagine, is quite disturbing and can and does lead to a multitude of symptoms.

Even a very fast and shock like, unexpected bereavement has indeed the same characteristics as any form of bereavement – only they are very fast and the stretching, tearing, regrouping doesn't appear to have happened at all.

For such occurrences, it is essentially helpful to work with the original shock in minute detail, using, for example, the story protocol. This is a way of slowing down time and stretching the original shock occurrence out into its components. By doing so you are not only cleanly healing the aspects (and there can be many!) of the original experience, but also track the development of the bereavement processes which we are always intending to move on, forward and through to their final conclusion.

Time-Energy Displacements

Time – and especially displaced time – is our final consideration in the treatment of bereavement related problems. You may be familiar with one of the main indicators of Post Traumatic Stress Disorder or PTSD which are memory flashbacks where the individual is literally **re-living** a part of the experience over and over again, as though it was happening NOW and not in the past where it belongs. There are numerous ways in which we can represent an individual's time of life to ourselves so we can manipulate this in consciousness at the energetic levels.

One of the most common representations would be that of a time-LINE that consists of all the individual's experiences and states of being, in physicality as well as on all the levels that work with linear time and where this makes sense and is correct. I personally have the notion of a time line that is a spiral around the central Unchanging You – much like the galaxies model, in fact, only more rounded and multi-dimensional. In general, we orientate ourselves in such a way that the past is to the side and then behind us, beneath us as it gets further into the linear past, and the future ahead. With displaced time chunks or parts of the time line that have literally been exploded because of high emotion or shock, these chunks can be:

- Pushed right outside the system that is the individual and cause gaps and the same types of problems you would find in the "misplaced parts" section. This is the case with "repressed" or

271

"forgotten" memories or blank points of the highest trauma times.

- They can orbit erratically and strike at any time as is the case with PTSD,

- or even worse still, can become fixed right in front of the awareness point, thus becoming a constant and ever present NOW of a horror that rightfully belongs in the past.

Returning A Chunk Of Time

Firstly, you need to get an understanding of the piece of time that is causing the problem. Where is it? Where does it need to go? To discuss this with the client gives a real sense of what needs to be accomplished and a target to the sessions and approaches; and of course, this will be our test as well. We will know that the healing has been accomplished when the displaced "time chunk" has fitted right into the time line again and is connected to the time before and the time after as any normal memory would be. When we consider the question of, "Why has this (memory, emotion, event, experience) not returned to where it belongs?", not only will we find the correct opening statements which will accomplish exactly this ("It was too painful." – "I wish this had never happened at all." – "I want no part of this." – "Because it destroyed me."), but also we become aware of any possible systems having grown around and woven into the displaced time piece – if it is at all reachable and still within the energy system, it usually makes organic connections to other systems (and, and especially in the case of displaced time chunks, pulls the whole system out of shape in so doing).

Should you find this, you might need to gently dis-connect these holding strands (aspects, beliefs, further emotions, emotions-about-emotions, rationalisations etc) first so that the time chunk is free to move towards its original position.

In some cases, you might find that there is a real **pulling towards** putting the time chunk where it belongs as the time line system is eager to complete and restore itself; if there is a lot of resistance, here is our chance to really catch all the aspects and related constructs until the energetic entity which is the memory has found its rightful time and place within the system.

Please refer to the section in "Guiding Stars" how to test and reconnect these displaced pieces to make sure the memory is fully within the flow of "what happened before, what happened then, what happened next" to complete this healing approach.

The Final Stage – The Immortal Beloved

I am quite sure that our physicality is but an echo of something else that exists in a timeless space across the levels. I am not sure if this something else is what is called in general usage "the soul" or if the soul is but another echo of something much, much more profound that encompasses all the levels **and including all the physicalities** throughout all their times of life in The Hard AND all the incarnations. Either way, anyone who has successfully completed a full bereavement cycle to its rightful and Even Flow conclusion will know that there is a connection that remains to the individual, and it is not a connection of sadness or loss, but one of an admiration and gratitude and grace that it is really hard to put into words.

In the standard psychology style "Steps to Human Bereavement" it is deemed to be normal to have "anniversary flashbacks of sadness and despair". I would suggest that this is not at all the final step but simply an indication that the Bereavement Cycle was not completed in all ways yet – no doubt there are still misplaced chunks of time and mixed up parts remaining energetically and their corresponding wounds that cannot heal. **The True End of the Bereavement Cycle** is to be charged with joy and deepest gratitude when one remembers the individual – unconditionally, and profoundly, with not a trace of sadness, not a trace of regret, nothing but a pure celebration of having been lucky enough to have had a relationship with such an individual. Indeed, it **is a true cycle** because it returns back to that state of love, that state of falling in love and ***being in love*** only this time, it is forever.

Thus, every successfully completed bereavement energises you, lifts you and makes your life more worthwhile; every new relationship entered into with the view of its cycles and ending in this state of unconditional love to complete the cycle makes you **more** than you were in every sense of the word—more completed, more wise, and more loved.

I would encourage you to seek to move on any bereavement cycles of your own towards that direction – possibly with the help of other energy healers to cover your own blind spots when dealing with your own systems – and to work towards this outcome with any of your clients; indeed, to **accept nothing less** as the end result of the process of bereavement.

The EFT Evil CD Protocol

This is a breakthrough pattern from EmoTrance which, once again, can easily be backwardly engineered to bring relief to problems for all who know the simple classic EFT protocol.

Very simply put, we acquire ereas or thoughtfields into our energy body over the course of our lifetimes which are not our own but were simply put there by someone or something else. These specific, non-self originated ereas have the codename of "evil CDs" - in reference to the metaphor of someone coming along and pushing one of their CDs into your internal stereo against your will, wishes, desires and often even entirely without your knowledge.

Unfortunately, what happens when a foreign erea is "inserted" into the energy body, is that it then structurally becomes **a part of the energy body**.

As such, all the protection devices for survival the energy body has are now also extended to the foreign erea and a person starts to think of this erea now being theirs.

For example, someone might shout at a child, "You are useless."

The "evil CD" thus generated enters the child's energy body and gets stuck there because children do not yet have the channels to handle this kind of energy.

When the evil CD plays again and says, "You are useless" as was recorded indelibly upon it, because it plays now **on the inside**, the child will think, "**I** am useless".

When someone tries to get rid of the evil CD by, for example saying, "No you are not useless, let go of that thought.", the protective devices which lovingly protects **everything** and fiercely, to the very bitter end, **that is of that child**, will defend the cuckoo in the nest just as much as it would defend itself if someone threatened to cut off an arm, or gouge out an eye.

In the meantime, the child grows up, still believing that they themselves believe they are useless, and they will of course wonder why and try and make sense of this.

They will collect evidence to have it be right, behave within the parameters to make what the evil CD is playing and which they mistakenly believe to be **their** song logical and understandable. They might even enter therapy to explore just how it was they came to that conclusion and formed this kind of negative self construct which grew around the evil CD as the callus forms around an injury.

Now, unfortunately there is a misconception in personal development about "taking responsibility for all you are" - and this is a true tragedy in the case of the evil CDs.

This is like being stopped by the police and a kilo of cocaine is found in the trunk of your car but you never put it there yourself.

Putting your hand up in a court of law and accepting responsibility for the presence of the cocaine will not lead to becoming a better person, only to a very long prison sentence that is entirely undeserved, entirely unfair and entirely unjust.

The simple fact is that there is NO responsibility at all on the part of the child who was told that they were useless.

That evil CD is not theirs, it never was and no responsibility for having it there can or should ever be taken.

There is only one single response to evil CDs and that is to reject them totally and absolutely, in every way.

When this is done, it gives the command to energetically expel the evil CD from the person's energy system and, once outside, can simply be destroyed in any way possible or let go of in any way you want to because it is no longer protected by the energy body's defences of self.

How To Tell An Evil CD

Interestingly, this is extremely simple.

The totality is absolutely loving and absolutely protective of itself, and that is mind, body, spirit, energy system and whatever else there may be to the "totality that is one single human being".

There never is and there never was any kind of self sabotage, neither in the physicality nor anywhere else, and any kind of "self destructive" activity is simply due to the confusion of what is self, and what is not.

People make this a great deal worse because they desperately and automatically try to make a logic and a sense out of their thoughts, behaviours and problems in the context of their environments.

In order to explain just why they would think themselves useless, they will come up with all kinds of rationalisations, explanations, theories, ideas - right down to, "It's my karmic path and God's will that I should be useless in this lifetime."

All of that strengthens the internal bonds with the evil CD and makes it seem more and more as though it really was of the very fabric of self - and the more it becomes of the fabric of self (or self concept, self construct, if you will) the more it will be defended and the less it will respond to therapy, healing or any other approach designed to get rid of it.

To make it very simple, anything at all that is not absolutely and passionately loving, absolutely and passionately generative, and absolutely and passionately supportive to your totality is an evil CD and could be nothing else.

You would never say to someone you truly loved and wanted to have the longest, most fulfilled and happiest life possible, "You are useless!", would you?

Of course not.

And neither would your totality.

It would not berate you, frighten you, bring you down, undermine you at all, not now, not ever, not in its wildest dreams.

Now, we have to tell our energy systems and our totality to revoke the protection of the evil CDs and absolutely reject them from our systems, and using EFT we do this with the following opening statement:

I absolutely reject the idea that I am useless and I deeply and profoundly love and accept myself.

Other variants are:

I was never useless and I will never be useless and I deeply ...

There nothing about me that was ever useless and I deeply ...

... or any words that would come spontaneously to you in response to understanding that none of those things in your self construct that were so blatantly cruel, limiting and unloving could EVER have come from your loving totality.

Aspects & Ancient Support Structures

When you start to treat evil CDs with absolute rejection, their related aspects and of course, the support structures your system has built around them for all these years, will come to the fore.

For example, the person who was told they were useless might think, "But if I thought I wasn't useless anymore, then I would have to do a lot of hard work all of a sudden. I better not reject the uselessness outright because it might save me from things, protect me from things."

That is absolute nonsense and of course, could only be thought by someone who thought they were useless - incapable of facing all challenges that could come their way from a centre of strength, safe and supported by their totality in all ways.

These kinds of thoughts that the evil CDs which make up our appalling self constructs and strangle all joy from our lives are somehow good, valuable or needed are nothing but ancient support structures to make the constant sore that is an evil CD liveable with at all in the first place.

These thoughts are the calluses which form around a pressure point to prevent further damage and they need to be removed and rejected, dismantled and abolished just as cleanly and powerfully as the evil CDs themselves.

Interestingly, these aspects and ancient support structures fall away and into silence one by one if you simply keep on rejecting the original evil CD - I am not and I was never useless and I deeply and profoundly love and accept myself.

The Evil CD Protocol - Conclusion

I have written many protocols over the years and I have had many, many breakthrough insights on how things work, but I must say that as simple as this is, this is one of my favourite protocols of all time.

278

What we all need as human beings is really, just one single person to be absolutely on our side, to really love us, help us, protect us, inspire us, applaud us when we have succeeded in something, no matter how insignificant it may seem to an outsider, someone who will encourage us to strive towards the best we can possibly be, cheer us on; someone who cannot ever be tempted away by youth, beauty, money, bribes and will always choose us, every day, each moment afresh; someone to stand by us when everything falls apart, love us no matter what; someone who will never let us down, never give up on us, never leave us and who will always, always be fiercely and actively loving of us in every way, every day, until we take our last breath in physicality.

Well, that person is here. It is you. And now, finally, we can start on the road to be that person we always knew we should have been - with a little help from our self, our endlessly loving totality.

And ... EFT.

True Forgiving With EFT

Most if not all psychology and spiritual treatments constantly exhort the necessity of "forgiving" those who caused you injury in order to be free of the past.

What they don't tell you is just **HOW** you are supposed to do that.

Forgiveness is not a process but an end result, a statement of "health regained", an effect but not a cause.

To seek this effect is healthy - but how can you forgive when you are still in daily pain because of what happened, what someone did to you, what you did to yourself?

The simple answer is that we are asking the impossible.

To ask someone who is still hurting to forgive those who hurt them is like telling a man with broken legs to walk and then climb to the top of a magic mountain where his broken legs will finally be healed.

It is impossible, it is cruel and it will hurt him even more in the process.

What we need to do is to talk about healing first, and when we do, we find that forgiveness follows suit swiftly, sweetly and completely, without any further heartache, headache or need for therapy.

How DO we heal these injuries?

How come that time hasn't healed the pain? Why is it that the body regrew new skin and new tissue, and now you can't tell that once this child had broken bones from the daily beatings, that once that woman was raw and bleeding from her rape if you just looked at their outside appearance?

What is it that has remained **unhealed** for all this time, is still raw and sore just as it was back then - what is it that causes the constant pain that simply makes "forgiveness" an impossibility?

The answer to this comes from the newest approaches in Energy Therapies.

Simply put, we have an energy body and this energy body sustains injuries just as well as the physical body does at the time of the incident, accident, attack, occurrence.

But unlike the physical body which grows and lives under the rules of the mechanical universe, this energy body doesn't heal through time because it lives in a timeless quantum space, where here and there are quite the same, and now and yesterday are no different than 20 years ago, 50 years ago, a lifetime ago.

Time does not heal the energy body.

Ordinary medicine does not heal the energy body either and that is why the wounds from the attack closed all that time ago with the physical treatment that was given and the physical body's own powers of restoration and growth through time is now no longer visible, or has become a faint scar as the years have passed, yet the energy body remains unhealed and sends its signals of pain through the medium of emotions and sensations that seem to have no rhyme or reason, no cause or effect in this consensus reality of ours which simply ignores all that cannot be seen to be measured.

To heal the invisible scars of the past, we must heal the injuries of the energy body.

Then the pain will stop and our minds and spirits return to a place of quiet, of tranquillity and peace where we understand perfectly what happened and why it happened, even understand the perpetrators and why they did what they did - but it is now really in the past where it so rightfully belongs, has belonged all this time in truth.

How Do I Heal My Energy Body?

At the most simple of all the levels, an awareness that such healing needs to take place is the very first step towards a true recovery process - recovering your balance, your power and your equilibrium, re-gaining a state we call the Even Flow where all is as it was designed to be.

In the energy healing modality of EmoTranceTM, which is specifically designed to heal ONLY the energy body, we first localise the erea of injury - we find the old wound.

This does not entail guesswork or intuition - we simply ask, when you think of THAT, where do you feel the pain in YOUR body?

People will hold their middles, put their hands before their eyes, clasp them to their heart, cup their jaw or hold their head in their hands in response. Of course they know where it hurts! That is where the injury is, plain for all to know and all to see.

And once we know **where** the injury is located, we can begin to heal it - with Reiki, with Therapeutic Touch, with Hands On Healing and with the techniques and methods from EmoTranceTM. What makes this so profoundly effective and releasing, so amazingly soothing and gentle too is that the intention of healing is directed to the energy body, exactly to the place and part of your system which needs this restoration.

Unlike trying to heal an injured knee in this way, the energy body was always designed to respond to **healing energy** and indeed it could be said that when physical injuries get better because of an application of energy healing, this is but a side effect in truth of what went on at a much deeper level.

In healing "the emotional wounds of the past", healing the energy body is a thousand times more effective than in healing the physical body which lives under the rules of the mechanical universe and needs time, substances, vitamins, processes that unfold in order to come back to ordinary functioning.

The energy body needs just healing energy and intention to repair the wounds and it isn't bound by time and space - it can and does respond **immediately** to this attention and these energies being directed its way at last.

It is simply so that no-one seems to remember to heal the energy body too at the time of accidents and incidence and all healing intention at the time seems so totally focussed on the physical alone - it is understandable.

But the fact remains that we now have the means at our disposal to really heal the past, and when we do, forgiveness too comes into being naturally and as a direct result of having restored The Even Flow.

Indeed, you can turn it around and actively use any areas of your life where you know you can't and won't forgive to show you where your old energetic injuries are located, using your "unforgivingness" as a diagnostic tool to show you the way to true and real freedom from the past, real and true peace of mind at last.

Reaching The State of True Forgiving With EFT

The above was a general article I wrote in order to explain what forgiveness – or should I say, reaching the state and experience of having truly forgiven something or somebody – actually is and to leave it open for the general reader to find their own way and path towards healing these energetic injuries which are still causing the pain by whichever modality they would choose to approach this task.

Here, as an advanced EFT pattern, we are going to use the states of anger and non-forgiving as the diagnostic tool to lead us straight to the energetic injuries which must be healed.

In order to do this, we start by asking the following question.

"What has happened to you in the past that should never be forgiven?"

Please note the phrasing of "should".

As is always the case, someone who is still hurting and furiously angry is deeply congruent and convinced at the conscious level that they must remain in this state and will of course, **protect** this conviction with various rationalisations that arise logically from this underlying conviction, such as, "They don't deserve to be forgiven." – "If I forgave them, they would do it again." – "It would make my suffering meaningless." – "Only if they are made to suffer the same as I did, can my own suffering be ever healed or alleviated."

Of course, there are many, many variations of the above, and really, there is no point in treating any of them because although they might briefly take the edge off the feelings, they are nothing but symptoms in themselves and are being endlessly generated from the underlying injury and the convictions this injury has forged over time.

If you or the client feel it is absolutely necessary, you can tap on those kinds of objections to loosen the system for a while but just be sure to note that this isn't what is stopping us from reaching the state of true forgiveness by itself and that even if you go down this road, to be absolutely aware that the real work still remains to be done.

To return to our original question of, "What has happened in the past that should never be forgiven?", in return your client will of course tell you what did happen.

Hear them out and really let them tell you in their own words, in the strongest of terms the real truth and feelings they have on the topic. This is a time for them to take off the bandages and excuses, they do not have to be nice and enlightened or even logical for indeed if they were, we would not be able to judge the real true extend of the injuries that were received, nor be able to really get down to healing these.

What we will get to hear is about people who have caused these injuries – individual people or perhaps at first, collections of people and the client's feelings about these people.

This is our first real work in treating the true injuries, namely to elicit from the client how they really feel about (that man, my mother, God, society, the law) etc.

For example, people might say things like:

- "They let me down and I HATE THEM for it."
- "They left in the darkness and I have been terrified ever since."

These are our first, true, full on opening statements to bring about a healing and re-alignment which will, eventually lead to the state of clarity and freedom that is so desirable, important, a true turning point at which a person becomes finally FREE of the past and now have a future once more when before, they did not.

Collections Of Injuries & Pain

Generally, once we have started to repair the first presenting emotions, such as anger and fury, others will present themselves naturally. One thought beyond the anger and one which shows us that we are getting somewhere in healing these old, infected injuries now which have caused so many secondary effects which all brought yet more pain and dissolution to the system is as follows:

"I just cannot understand why they did that to me."

Clients will express this complete failure to make sense of the world that occurred as the results of their experiences in many different ways; but this kind of statement is one of the last remaining barriers to successful resolution.

In order to answer that very question, people have searched a lifetime and made theories to explain this because if there was an explanation, some kind of road to the future could be planned once the lesson of the event was actually understood and made some sense.

If this doesn't happen, a major part of an individual's "map of the universe" is missing and they are left in chaos and confusion.

Some answer that central question with statements such as, "It was God's will." or, "It was because I did something really bad in a past life." Other variations include, "It was because there is something terribly wrong with me." or, "It was because this world is hell in truth and that's why things like that happen randomly."

It is important to note that once again, these collections of meanings and justifications are symptoms because they are generated from the underlying question which was never successfully answered.

As with the justification statements pertaining to not being allowed or able to start the processes leading towards forgiveness at all, one can tap on those for a very long time and not find any major relief in the presenting symptoms as simply more are being generated from the original question – forever, if necessary.

In Advanced EFT Forgiveness, what we need to do is **to find the question** and use that question for the opening statement and of course, to hear what answers the client is producing **after** the treatment in order to test the movement in the systems and to find whatever is left to treat.

Proof Of Healing - The Forgiveness State

EFT can relieve the pressing symptoms quite quickly, even if the true energetic injuries have not been entirely healed. The client will say, "I feel much better, ok, I'm ready to forgive them all now.", most likely because they too have heard time and time again that it is "good to

286

forgive" and that if you are a decent person, that's what you **have to do** in order to buy your piece of health and happiness at last.

Therapists too have urged their clients on, even unconsciously, to say those words as a "proof of healing" because of course, they want to know that their client has indeed, completed the healing process – that's what every healer wants and therapists are healers really, even if some are not quite aware of that yet.

For us, it is very different.

There is only one single proof of healing, and that is of the client entering the state of forgiveness.

This is not about something they say alone, but something they **feel** and something that you can see, hear, sense and feel in your entire body as well when you are in the presence of it.

It is an extraordinary state of clarity and true release. The client will look and feel wide awake. They may be speechless. They may be astonished and express a sense of, "I can't believe this! This is so **very different!**" They may try and find within themselves any remaining objections, sense of the pain, injustice, anger, confusion etc which had been their constant companions for so long and these things are simply not there anymore.

Here, once again, it is essential to not throw the client out because the bell has just rung and "time's up!". Like an operation takes exactly as long as it takes to complete it and no-one would dream of simply stopping with the patient still on the table and their chest cavity not having been stitched up, our healing doesn't finish successfully until we have discussed with the client how they feel now, what they can think of to replace those activities which revolved around the pain, and to have them stable and pro-active before we call it a day.

Sending a client off who has just had a major epiphany without tying their experience successfully into their past and future can and does lead to all sorts of problems, including the dreaded apex effect and of course, our equivalent of the "freshly healed wound becoming infected". Further, the conscious constructs which have grown around the original wound are often still in place and continue to generate thoughts and behaviours even in the absence of the original problem and you can imagine how very confusing that is when the client has not been properly prepared, centreed and grounded before they return to their ordinary environments.

It is always useful but in cases of deep healing, as we are doing with Forgiveness work, it is essential to explain this to the client and to include in their homework protocols ways of dealing with these old remaining construct thoughts, and to discuss generative opening statements which will support their emergence into an entirely new and different state of being, a different life altogether.

ADDENDUM – ESSENTIAL CLASSIC EFT REVIEW

The Classic EFT Protocol

Just in case you found this book on a train, here is a basic EFT protocol so the rest of this book makes at least some sense.

However, you need to read "Adventures In EFT" which contains the basic patterns of working with EFT and all the ground level protocols.

Classic EFT uses 14 major meridian points, which are generally at the start or the end of a major body meridian. Here they are:

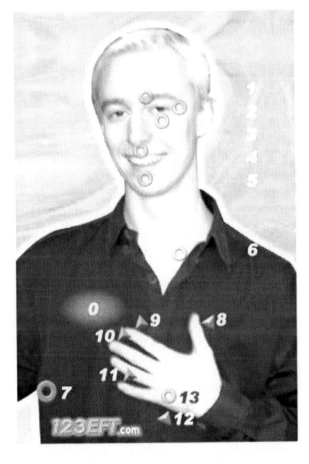

0 = The Sore Spot - On your chest where you would pin a medal or a brooch. Gently push with your fingertips to find an area that feels tender, rather than sore.

1 = Start Of The Eyebrow - Where the bone behind your eyebrow turns into the bridge of your nose.

2 = Corner Of The Eye - On the bone in the corner of your eye.

3 = Under The Eye - On the bone just below your eye, in line with your pupil if you look straight ahead.

4 = Under Nose - Between you nose and your upper lip

5 = Under The Mouth - In the indentation between your chin and your lower lip

6 = Collarbone - In the angle formed by your collarbone and the breastbone

7 = Under Arm - in line with a man's nipples, side of the body

8 = Thumb - all finger points are on the side of the finger, in line with the nail bed.

9 = Index Finger, 10 = Middle Finger, 11 = Little Finger

12 = Karate Chop Point - on the side of your hand, roughly in line with your life line.

13 = Gamut Point - just behind and between the knuckles of your ring and little finger.

Classic EFT - The Whole Treatment At A Glance

Step 1 - Name the problem, clearly, directly and truthfully.

Step 2 - Take a SUDs reading of how bad it is right now 0-10

Step 3 - Do the Set Up - "Even though I have this problem, I deeply and profoundly accept myself" three times out loud, whilst rubbing the Sore Spot or tapping on the Karate Chop point to correct for any possible Psychological Reversal.

Step 4 - Choose a shortened "reminder phrase" and say this on each point as you tap from the top of the eyebrow to the karate chop point.

Step 5 - Do the 9 Gamut procedure (eyes left to right, up to down, in a circle, hum/count/hum) whilst tapping or holding the Gamut point.

Step 6 - Do another round with the reminder phrase as in Step 4.

Step 7 - Take a deep breath in and out and take a new SUDs reading.

Subsequent Rounds - Change the Set Up to:

> **Even though there is still some of this problem remaining, I deeply and profoundly accept myself.**

… and finally to:

> **I want to get completely over this problem and I deeply and profoundly accept myself.**

… to get your problem right down to 0.

Essential Classic EFT Patterns Review

Contacting The Problem

The Prime Directive:

ONLY THE CLIENT CAN KNOW THE RIGHT WORDS!

Opening Statements

1. The Statement Approach

The problem at the level of the symptom:

"Even though I have this problem, ..."

2. Investigating Root Causes

Trying to pin point the root cause for generative change.

"Even though I don't know why I have this problem ..."

(memory flashes, pre-memories, "ideas & "thoughts", body sensations)

3. Trigger Approach

Objects & Substances, Photographs, Music, Film.

4. Keyword Approach

Disassociate the problem memory by using a code word, key word, number, symbol or colour ("Tearless Trauma Technique")

5. Checklist Approach

Anti-Affirmations, Wellness Beliefs

"Even though I am not a child of the universe ..."

6. Non-Directive Tapping

Overwhelm, depression, pain, trance states

"I deeply & profoundly accept myself"

Classic Protocols Review

Keyword Protocol

1. Choose key word, symbol or number to represent the problem/trigger/memory. Note the more abstract the key is, the less the emotional charge will be. "This rape memory" has a much higher charge than "This blue memory" or "This 3 memory".

2. Proceed with the normal treatment protocol until the test on the key phrase is positive and it no longer holds any emotional charge.

3. Help client find further keywords for any remaining aspects. Note if it is now possible to become more specific.

4. Continue with steps 1-4 until you can test the original event/memory/trigger without encoding and there is no more emotional response.

Story Protocol

1. Have client tell the story of the event/memory/trigger.

2. Stop as soon as any emotional disturbance is detected and tap on the last statement the client made.

3. Test by having the client re-tell the story from the beginning; they should be able to go past the previous sticking point easily. If not, there are further aspects remaining.

4. When the client is completely calm on the first point, have them continue the story. Stop to treat each emotional disturbance.

5. The test is for the client to be able to tell the entire story from start to finish and remain calm (at 0) throughout.

Basic Metaphor Protocol

1. Elicit metaphor for presenting symptom/s: If this (pain, problem, blockage etc) had a colour/shape/size/weight, what would it be?

2. Use elicited metaphor (i.e. this big purple triangle) as the opening statement: Even though I have this big purple triangle in my back, ...

3. Track changes in the metaphor to track changes in the stuck state/presenting problem - is it getting smaller, lighter, moves somewhere else?

4. It is possible that at some point the metaphor releases into a real life memory, memory flashback, or the client may have a spontaneous insight as to the pattern or nature of the problem. You can then switch back to conventional opening statements if required.

5. The shift has occurred when the metaphor is dissolved, resolved or has become something pleasant, energising or desirable.

Basic Proxy Protocol

1. Switching to first person perspective on another person, a part of the self or a problem itself.

2. Formulate statement beginning with "I am (Peter)." and the rest of the opening statement as usual: "I am Peter. Even though I have this problem, I deeply and profoundly love and accept myself."

3. Before testing, re-enter the "switched state" by stating again: "I am (Peter)."

CONCLUSION: BEYOND EFT

Now, here we are at the end of "The Advanced Patterns of EFT".

As certain things already show, there are of course dimensions of mind-body totality healing we have not even thought to touch or investigate properly.

There are many hints of totally other states of being, other ways of experiencing anything all through the application of EFT – just classic EFT and nothing more! – to common human problems.

In the summer of 2002, I developed something that takes the base learnings from all the many, many EFT sessions and approaches I had worked with and, going back to the drawing board completely, shows a new way of dealing with disturbances in the Energy Body.

This new way is called EmoTrance, or ET for short.

It is both far simpler and far more complicated than EFT. It is simply **other** than EFT and it was my pleasure in preparing this book to really come face to face with how **other** EmoTrance actually really is, because it arises from very different propositions about how humans work in their totality and what needs to be done to restore "The Even Flow" – a human's energy system firstly working again as it was originally designed to be working.

However, I will not now nor will I ever either forget or forget to give credit and the most inordinate respect to EFT and its originator, Gary Craig, who gave me the tool I needed to make EmoTrance.

The funniest thing of all at the very end of this book is to say that EmoTrance simply makes most of the patterns here redundant.

However, I appreciate that I came to EmoTrance via exactly these patterns and in performing these advanced patterns and working with them, I pushed the existing paradigm to its limits. When those limits broke under the strain, I learned how to do it differently altogether.

I would therefore invite you to use these patterns, with all due respect and care and all the disclaimers, because they are the bridge from EFT to EmoTrance and that whole **other** map of the world and the magic you will find therein.

I sincerely hope that the students of EmoTrance now and in the future will not only read about these patterns, but actually do some of them because they hold the proof in actuality of why and how EmoTrance works and that knowing about these patterns and understanding them will deepen their own connection between the original psychology precepts and what we are dealing with now.

Such an understanding is in my opinion vital at this stage in order to allow people to move from the old to the new without a sense of loss, without experiencing apex effect because it is simply too mind blowing to shift paradigm without some form of stepping stone system to help make that necessary and in the end, inevitable transition.

I would also further invite you as you work with these patterns to always retain a sense of the question, "What do they all have in common?", for these patterns here are just a minute proportion of what I could have written about. In answering this question, or even just attempting to answer it, lies breath-taking progress into whole new possibilities of growth, change, healing and most importantly, a state of being for humans that is so **other** from what we have been shown these last 100,000 years or more, that you could even say – at last , there's hope.

With best regards to you on your path,

Silvia Hartmann

December 9th, 2002

FURTHER INFORMATION

About The Author

Silvia Hartmann PhD is a highly qualified and experienced trainer of Hypnosis, Hypnotherapy, Energy Therapies and Neuro-Linguistic Programming, author, international lecturer and motivational speaker. She is the Co-Founder and Director of The Association For Meridian & Energy Therapies and founder of the oldest established MET internet newsgroup, Meridiantherapy, as well as being a Contributing Editor to Gary Craig's EmoFree List.

With an extensive record in trainings design, she is well known for her outstanding ability to create trainings that allow the participants to understand and integrate even highly complex materials and making it easy to learn, easy to do and easy to replicate.

She is the author of numerous highly acclaimed original works in the field, including "Project Sanctuary" and "Guiding Stars 2002".

Silvia Hartmann's best-selling EFT Training Manual "Adventures In EFT" has to date been translated into four languages and is acknowledged to be "The Best Book on EFT".

After studying and re-searching Energy Psychology & Meridian Energy Therapies approaches in-depth for four years, Silvia Hartmann created EmoTrance™, a truly groundbreaking and entirely innovative approach to working with the human energy system for mental and physical health.

For Further Information about Silvia's Work please visit:

http://sidereus.org - News & Library Portal Of The Sidereus Foundation

http://starfields.org - Complete Online Catalogue of Manuals & Trainings

http://dragonrising.com - Hard Copy Books, Courses, CDs etc.

http://emotrance.com - The EmoTrance™ News & Library Portal

Adventures In EFT

Adventures In EFT is the World's best selling guide for beginners to Gary Craig's Emotional Freedom Techniques EFT.

Now in its fifth revised edition, Adventures does not require any previous knowledge of healing, counselling, psychology or human health or changework at all – anyone who can read can pick up this book and start to make their lives feel a whole lot better, right away.

Yet, in spite of Adventures' easy to read, friendly and informative style, all the base patterns of EFT are here – modelled on Gary Craig himself and with additional modelling from the leading EFT therapists in the World, Adventures is also a fine handbook for any healer or counsellor wishing to begin to make use of the extraordinary powers of EFT to make profound changes in people's lives.

Sparkling with ideas, enthusiasm and lively suggestions for how to take the Classic EFT protocols and make them come to life for you.

Adventures In EFT

The Essential Field Guide To

Emotional Freedom Techniques

by Silvia Hartmann, PhD

ISBN 1 873483 63 5

Available from
http://DragonRising.com - 44 1323 729 666
and all good bookshops.

The Advanced Patterns Of EFT

Primarily for professional therapists, psychologists and students and researchers in the field of Meridian & Energy Therapies, The Advanced Patterns of EFT by Silvia Hartmann, PhD, re-writes the limits of what used to be.

The first part of this advanced manual concentrates on the EFT treatment flow and describes essential patterns, techniques and variations on the Classic EFT process which move an EFT treatment into the realms of true quantum healing.

The second part consists of the advanced patterns themselves – treatment guides, techniques and approaches for guilt, bereavement, high end addictions, parts healing, shamanic applications and the original Guiding Stars patterns, released for the first time.

The Advanced Patterns Of EFT is an outstanding, original contribution to the emergent field of Meridian & Energy Therapies and an invaluable resource to any serious student, practitioner and researcher in the field.

The Advanced Patterns Of EFT

by Silvia Hartmann, PhD

ISBN 1 873483 68 6

Available from
http://DragonRising.com - 44 1323 729 666
and all good bookshops.

Oceans Of Energy - The Patterns & Techniques of EmoTrance™

For most people, EFT is all they could ask for and all they ever need to smooth out their lives and be able to do and be so much more than they ever thought possible.

I've learned so much by working with EFT this closely for four years, and as a result of what I have learned, I have designed EmoTrance – a stand-alone Energy Healing system for those who wish to work with the human energy body in a more personal, more intimate way.

EmoTrance™ re-connects the user with their bodies and their own being in a profound and lasting way. It is an outstanding self help tool not just to remove old injuries but also to manage new states that arise all the time, there and then, so they need never become future incidents for us to have to tap on.

EmoTrance™ is further a superb healing technique when a healer and a client align in their intention to produce a change – entirely client driven, entirely respectful of one individual human's personal perceptions and experiences in this World, it is fast, gentle and deeply profound in all applications.

Lastly, EmoTrance™ is designed to teach us about our own intuition, our own energy systems and that of others, our "energy nutritional requirements" and what energy healing really is at the end of the day.

If you have worked with EFT and you are ready to step beyond into a whole new world of living today and creating tomorrow, we invite you to take a closer look.

Oceans Of Energy

The Patterns & Techniques Of EmoTrance™ Volume 1

by Silvia Hartmann, PhD

ISBN 1 873483 73 2

Available from
http://DragonRising.com - 44 1323 729 666
and all good bookshops.

Project Sanctuary III

So now, we are working with the energy body, with thoughtfields, with meridians and energy shields and in the Quantum spaces where what we have learned about time, gravity, distance and more is no longer applicable. If we go into those spaces with our limited four-dimensional thinking, formed by the cause-and-effects of the physicality and after a lifetime of conditioning in the Hard, we will never be able to be at home here, never be able to actually **understand** and never mind affect these spaces and their processes as we should and as we can.

What is required is to learn a whole new way of thinking.

A logic based on entirely different principles, on entirely different laws of nature – quantum logic. Project Sanctuary is probably the first training manual ever written in the history of humanity to be a self help guide and device to teach quantum logic and to make it easy for anyone who wishes to learn.

Fascinating from the start, utilising immediately what we have remaining by the way of connection to our intuition, creativity, magic and the wider realms of the universe, Project Sanctuary is easy.

Indeed, it is surprisingly easy and what so many find so much more surprising still is the fact that this is not head-hurting school learning at all but exciting, fun, stimulating, sexy, funny, breath-takingly amazing and on occasion frighteningly exciting, too.

And that IS our first lesson in quantum logic – FORGET about learning being difficult or painful. FORGET THAT. That was learning the hard way and you can't learn hard amidst the flowing, glowing vibrant oceans of energy from which we came, and to which we will return in glory and delight, a homecoming of such wonder and awe, it will take your breath away.

For anyone seriously interested in getting really serious about learning, it's time to seriously lighten up and start learning for yourself, by yourself, in yourself – a one-on-one tuition between you and the universe itself. Project Sanctuary is your manual, handbook and tour guide - if you want it.

Project Sanctuary III

by Silvia Hartmann, PhD

ISBN 1 873483 98 8

Available from
http://DragonRising.com - 44 1323 729 666
and all good bookshops.

Certification Trainings In Meridian & Energy Therapies

The METs (which include EFT) are a whole new form of working with human mind-body problems. This being so, and in recognition of the fact that MET practitioners derive from all and every helping profession, allopathic and holistic, psychologists and body workers, hypnotherapists and healers, nurses and social workers included, the syllabus of the AMT Practitioner training includes essential knowledge of the protocols and practical hands on procedures in this new healing field.

Co-developed by the founder trainers of The AMT and trainings designed by Silvia Hartmann, PhD, the AMT Certification trainings represent state-of-the-art professional training which cannot be had elsewhere.

Silvia Hartmann also developed a correspondence course version of the live AMT training in order to open the possibility of gaining the benefits from this professional training to those who cannot personally attend a training.

To find a certified AMT practitioner or advanced practitioner, or for a list of training events, please go to http://theamt.com

Certified Practitioner/Certified Advanced Practitioner

Of Meridian & Energy Therapies

Professional Live Trainings & Distance Trainings

The Association For Meridian & Energy Therapies The AMT

http://TheAMT.com

Order The AMT Yearbook

Trainers & Practitioners Registers

Meridian & Energy Therapies Books

Events, Conferences & Organisations

Who's Who In Meridian Energy Therapies

EFT, TFT, TAT, ET, BSFF, HBLU, CHART, EDxTM

The Essential Guide To The New Energy Therapies

Available from
http://DragonRising.com - 44 1323 729 666
and all good bookshops.

Sources

The Energetic Relationships Set First Presented At Toronto Energy Psychology Conference November 2000.

Needs & Wants - First Published Meridiantherapy News Group April 2002.

Metaphors In MET Treatments - First Published AMT Energy E-Zine September 2000

Guiding Stars - First Published by DragonRising February 2000

Slow EFT - First Published by The AMT December 2001

The EFT Body Protocol - First Published Sidereus Foundation September 2002

The Inner Child Healing Spiral - First Published by The AMT April 2002

Creating A Shortcut Algorithm - First Published Meridiantherapy News Group September 2000

Addictions Protocol - First Published AMT MET Practitioner Training, 1999; this version MET Practitioner Correspondence Training, First Published DragonRising 2001

Energetic Bereavement - First Published In Energy Healing For Animals, The Sidereus Foundation, March 2001.

The Vortex Patterns - First Published The Sidereus Foundation, December 2001

Forgiveness – First Published The Sidereus Foundation December 2002